40 Biology Lab Activities

Written and Edited by G. Katz Chronicle
Publisher: IMNF Education Press, Pleasant Valley, NY
Copyright 2019
Library of Congress Control Number: 2022912554

Cover Design: G. Katz Chronicle

Thank you to Gloria Closi for the completion of jobs large and small.
Thank you to Sabrina Kee for her many skills.

Table of Contents

Biochemistry

Identifying Organic Compounds

Your instructor will provide you with the following materials: test tube, test tube rack, test tube holder, boiling water, spot plate, beaker, masking tape, brown wrapping paper, glucose solution, starch solution, oil (lipid), albumin solution, Benedict's solution, Biuret reagent, iodine, test tube brush, safety glasses

IDENTIFICATION OF CARBOHYDRATES

TEST FOR SUGAR: Place 10 drops of glucose solution and 10 mL of Benedict's solution in a clean test tube.

1-What is the color of the mixture of solutions?

_____

Label the test tube and place it in a boiling water bath for 5 minutes.

2-What color change occurs in the mixture of solutions after being heated?

_____

3-This change in color is a positive test that indicates the presence of:

_____

TEST FOR STARCH: Partly fill one of the depressions in the spot plate with starch solution. Partly fill another with water. Add 1 or 2 drops of iodine to each of the samples.

4-What color appears in the water sample after iodine has been added?

_____

5-What color change occurs in the starch solution after iodine has been added?

_____

6-The color change indicates a positive test result for the presence of:

_____

7-The water sample acts as a CONTROL. What is a control?

_____

_____

8-What is the purpose of the control?

_____

_____

IDENTIFICATION OF LIPIDS

GREASE SPOT TEST: Place a drop of oil to the left or right of center on the sheet of brown wrapping paper. Place a drop of water to the other side of center. Wait five minutes for the paper to dry and then hold the paper up to the light.

9-Which spot appears translucent after it dried?

_____

10-Paper turning translucent is a positive test for the presence of:

_____

IDENTIFICATION OF PROTEINS

BIURET TEST: Partly fill one of the depressions of the spot plate with egg albumin solution (protein). Partly fill another with water. Add 3-5 drops of Biuret reagent to each of these samples.

11-What color appears in the water sample?

_____

12-What color change occurs in the albumin?

_____

13-This change in color is a positive test that indicates the presence of:

_____

INDICATORS

Name which organic compound each of the following indicators would be used to test for:

14-BENEDICT'S SOLUTION	
15-IODINE	
16-GREASE SPOT TEST	
17-BIURET TEST	

Name_____ Date_____ Period_____ Lab_____

Investigating pH

Materials: Spot plate or small cups of substances with varying pH values, pH paper

An acid is any substance that yields hydrogen ions when put in solution. A base is any substance that accepts hydrogen ions in solution. A base added to an acidic solution makes that solution less acidic, while an acid added to a basic solution makes that solution less basic. At times the addition of an acid or base may cause a change in the nature of the substance.

The concentration of hydrogen ions in each solution determines how basic or acidic that solution is, as measured on the pH scale. This scale runs from 0 to 14, with 0 being most acidic, 14 being most basic, and 7 being neutral. Living things function best in a near-neutral pH, though some systems in living things have different pH requirements.

In this investigation, you will use pH of various substances and to explore the effect of an acid and base. You will also observe how a biological molecule is affected by a change in pH.

Part 1: Determine the pH of substances

- Fill in test substance row on data collection table.
- Obtain samples of substances with varying pH values
- Dip a small piece of pH indicator paper the test substance. Remove the strip from the substance and compare the color change to the reference card to determine the pH. Record the pH number on the data table.
- Repeat the previous step for each test substance.
- Complete the table by filling in the last row of information.

pH Investigation TABLE							
Well/Cup	1	2	3	4	5	6	7
Test Substance							
pH							
Acid, Base, or Neutral							

Conclusion Questions:

1-Define pH.

_____

_____

2-Which substances were acidic?

_____

_____

3-Which substances were basic?

_____

_____

4-Which of the substances were neutral?

_____

_____

Part 2: Observe the effect of a low pH on an organic compound

A. Partially fill two wells on a well plate with milk.
B. In one of the milk wells add six drops of distilled water; In the other add six drops of vinegar.
C. Gently mix the wells by gently shaking the well plate.
D. Test for pH levels, observe any change in the nature of the milk and record your findings in the data table.

Effect of Low pH on an Organic Compound TABLE		
Test Tube	Milk+ Distilled Water (1)	Milk+ Vinegar (2)
pH		
Acid, Base, or Neutral		
Describe nature of mixture		

Conclusion Questions:

5-What is the question being investigated?

_____

_____

6-Identify the control group.

_____

7-Identify the experimental group.

_____

8-What can you conclude from the results? Include what happened to the milk.

_____

_____

_____

Further Assessment:

9-Is the pH of all water the same? Explain your answer.

_____

_____

_____

10-A pond has a pH of 6 and its pH was rechecked after heavy rain to find it went down to a pH of 4. Did the pond become more acidic or more basic? By how much?

_____

_____

11-If one were to increase the pH of a solution what substance must be added to allow this increase to happen?

_____

_____

12-Why is pH important to all living things?

_____

_____

_____

13-Write the name of each substance you tested at the point along the scale that corresponds to its pH. Fully label the pH scale using your notes.

| 1 | 2 | 3 | 4 | 5 | 6 | 7 | 8 | 9 | 10 | 11 | 12 | 13 | 14 |

Molecular Modeling

Materials

Molecule Kit or Gumdrops (or other soft candy with a variety of colors) & toothpicks

Introduction

Organic compounds are those compounds that have the elements carbon and hydrogen bonded together. Carbohydrates, fats, and proteins are three major groups of organic compounds found in living things. They are composed mainly of the elements carbon, hydrogen, and oxygen. In proteins, nitrogen is also present. These elements bond together in organic compounds by sharing their electrons. The bond formed when atoms share electrons is known as a covalent bond.

1-What is an organic compound?

_____

_____

2-What are three major groups of organic compounds?

_____

3-Organic compounds are composed mainly of what three elements?

_____

_____

4-Proeins also contain what additional element?

_____

5-What is a covalent bond?

_____

6-Consult your notes. Indicate the number of bonding sites for each of these elements.

Hydrogen (H) _____   Carbon (C) _____

Oxygen (O) _____   Nitrogen (N) _____

7-Compounds composed entirely of carbon and hydrogen are called hydrocarbons. Ethane is a hydrocarbon that has the molecular formula C_2H_6. Draw the structural formula for ethane in the box below.

Organic Molecule Construction

Construct each of the following molecules using the molecule kit or colored candies and toothpicks. Use the key below for each of the elements listed. **Each of your molecule models must be checked by your instructor for credit.**

Alanine

Fructose

Fatty Acid

KEY

CARBON = BLACK   HYDROGEN = WHITE

OXYGEN = RED   NITROGEN = BLUE

Inorganic Molecule Construction

Place the names of the following molecules beneath their structural formulas.

$$O=O$$

$$H \overset{O}{\diagdown} H$$

$$O=C=O$$

8- _____   9- _____   10- _____

Construct each of the above molecules using the molecule kit or colored candies and toothpicks. Use the key above for each of the elements listed. **Have all three molecule models checked by your instructor for credit.**

11-Explain why fats, carbohydrates, and proteins are organic molecules and the three molecules on this page are not. (Hint: See number 1 of this lab.)

_____

_____

_____

_____

_____

_____

_____

_____

_____

_____

_____

Observing the Enzyme Catalase

MATERIALS PER GROUP:

forceps or tweezer, chopsticks or skewer, hydrogen peroxide (H_2O_2), matches or lighter, 6-8 test tubes, samples of liver in various treatments (room temperature, in hydrochloric acid (HCl), in sodium hydroxide (NaOH), pulverized, boiled, and frozen)

INTRODUCTION:

What would happen to your cells if they made a poisonous chemical? You might think they would die. In fact, your cells are always making poisonous chemicals. They do not die because your cells use enzymes to break down these poisonous chemicals into harmless substances. Enzymes are proteins that speed up the rate of reactions that would otherwise happen more slowly. The enzyme is not altered (1-_____) by the reaction. You have hundreds of different enzymes in each of your cells. Each of these enzymes is responsible for one particular reaction that occurs in the cell.

In this lab, you will study an enzyme that is found in the cells of many living tissues. The name of the enzyme is catalase (KAT-uh-LAYSS); it speeds up a reaction which breaks down hydrogen peroxide, a toxic chemical, into 2 harmless substances—water and oxygen. The reaction is as follows:

$$2H_2O_2 \longrightarrow 2H_2O + O_2$$

This reaction is important to cells because hydrogen peroxide (H_2O_2) is produced as a byproduct of many normal cellular reactions. If the cells did not break down the hydrogen peroxide, they would be poisoned and die.

In this lab you will study catalase found in liver cells. You will be using chicken or beef liver. It might seem strange to use dead cells to study the function of enzymes. This is possible because when a cell dies, the enzymes remain intact and active for several weeks, as long as the tissue is kept refrigerated.

In this lab, we will investigate how the enzyme catalase reacts under certain environmental conditions. One environmental condition is the pH. Another is temperature.

REVIEW pH:

pH is the measure of the acidity or alkalinity of a solution. An acidic solution has many hydrogen ions (H+) and a pH below 7. An alkaline or basic solution has very few hydrogen ions and a pH above 7. A neutral solution has a pH of 7.

2-Draw the pH scale in the space below. Show with arrows where the hydrogen ion concentration is increasing and where the hydrogen ion concentration is decreasing. Label acidic, neutral, and basic values.

Use indicator paper to determine the pH of the Hydrochloric Acid (HCl) and Sodium Hydroxide (NaOH). Record the pH values in the appropriate area of Table 2. Have your instructor initial here that pH values have been determined and recorded:

_____

Use goggles when using chemicals

Review Enzyme Lock and Key Models:

- A **substrate** is a molecule that an enzyme acts upon.
- The **reactants** are the molecules that join in a chemical reaction.
- The **products** are the molecules produced by the reaction.
- **Enzymes are reusable.**

3-Draw a "Lock and Key" Model:

If an enzyme has a large amount of **surface area,** the rate of the reaction will be increased. This is because more surface area allows the substrate to react with a larger amount of the active site of the enzyme. More enzyme-substrate complexes will be formed, thus increasing the product formation.

Under certain conditions enzymes can be **denatured (4-_____).** An enzyme is denatured when the protein molecule loses its proper shape and cannot function. Some things that can denature an enzyme are enzyme concentration, extremes in temperature, and extremes in pH. This lab will focus on varying temperature and pH.

PRACTICE PROCEDURE AND OBSERVATIONS

Use forceps, skewers, or chopsticks to position a piece of liver in a test tube (TT). Place 4mL H_2O_2 in the same TT. Hold the TT with your fingers so that you can both see and feel the reaction.

5-What is happening in the TT?

_____

6-What gas is being released?

_____

Reactions that absorb heat are **endothermic.** Reactions that give off heat are **exothermic.**

7-Did the TT get warmer or cooler?

_____

8-Was the reaction endothermic or exothermic?

_____

Use the following rating scale to quantify the rate of reaction observed:

0-No reaction

1-Slow

2-Slow to Moderate

3-Fast (produces froth/head)

4-Very Fast (produces froth/head that rises quickly)

Record of enzyme activity in room temperature liver:

Table 1: Practice Quantifying Reaction Rate on Room Temperature Liver

SAMPLE	RATE OF ENZYME ACTIVITY/SPEED OF BUBLES
Liver	

Is Catalase Reusable?

Dump the liquid out of the TT but retain the liver.

9-After the reaction, what was the liquid in the TT composed of? (see 1st page of lab).

_____

10-Add another 2 mL of H_2O_2 to the liver remaining in the first TT. Did you get similar reaction this time?

_____

11-Is the enzyme catalase within the liver reusable?

_____

Dispose of the liver used for this activity and put the TT in the sink.

You now know that the enzyme catalase in room temperature liver will react with the substrate hydrogen peroxide (H_2O_2) and create the products water (H_2O) and oxygen (O_2).

PROCEDURE:

You will now test to see how temperature, pH, and surface area affect enzyme activity. You will be observing the rate at which bubbles are created (quantified on a 0-4 scale) and the number of times a wooden splint (coffee stirrer) can be re-lit by the oxygen (O₂) produced during the reaction. Also note if there is an exothermic reaction for each test.

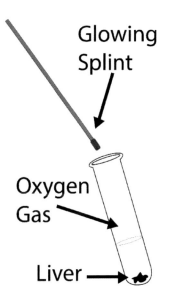

Glowing Splint

Oxygen Gas

Liver

Use goggles when using chemicals

A-For each test you will obtain and position the piece of liver at the bottom of a clean TT. (Wait until just before you are ready to begin the test to obtain liver for test 6 as it is important that it be frozen SOLID).

B-Light the splint with a match and gently blow the flame so that the wood is only glowing at the end.

C-AT THE SAME TIME, pour 2 mL of H_2O_2 into the TT.

D-QUICLY put the glowing splint into the TT where the reaction is occurring, but DO NOT PUT THE SPLINT INTO THE LIQUID.

E-If the splint re-lights, pull it out and gently blow on it until it is only glowing.

F-Do this repeatedly until the splint will no longer re-light.

G-Record your observations in **Table 2.**

Table 2: Observing the Reactions of the Enzyme Catalase in Liver

TEST	Liver	Bubbling Reaction Rate (0-4)	Number of Splint Re-lights	Exothermic Reaction (Y/N)
1	Room Temperature			
2	(Acidic) Hydrochloric Acid (HCl) pH: _____			
3	(Alkaline/Basic) Sodium Hydroxide (NaOH) pH: _____			
4	Pulverized (to Increase Surface Area)			
5	Boiled			
6	Frozen			

ANALYSIS:

12-What is an enzyme?

_____

_____

13-According to your results, what environmental conditions resulted in the most bubbling/highest number of re-lights (and, therefore, the most enzyme activity)?

_____

_____

14- According to your results, what environmental conditions resulted in the least bubbling/fewest number of re-lights (and, therefore, the least enzyme activity)?

_____

_____

15- What affect did changing the temperature and pH in tests 2, 3, 5, & 6 have on the shape of the catalase enzyme in the liver?

_____

_____

16-Why should test 4 have produced the most relights? (See 2nd page of lab)

_____

Cellular Energy

Cellular Respiration in Plants

Introduction

Plants make their own food by photosynthesis. What do plants do when there is no sunlight or during the night time? Do they starve for energy?

When plants do not have light available, they can also rely on Cellular Respiration to stay alive. Organisms from the plant kingdom are made up of eukaryotic cells. Therefore, they have mitochondria, the organelle responsible for cellular respiration.

Respiration requires the intake of oxygen and release of carbon dioxide. Animals breathe, plants don't. So how can the plant get oxygen? Oxygen from the air is able to diffuse into the plant cells that are in direct contact with the environment. Plants also have tiny air-holes called stomata or lenticels, where oxygen diffuses into the plant. The waste product of cellular respiration, Carbon dioxide, diffuses out of the plant cells by the same structures.

In this lab you will be able to detect the presence of carbon dioxide by using a pH indicator. The indicator, Bromthymol blue, changes color as carbon dioxide dissolves in water, forming carbonic acid. The reaction is illustrated in the chemical equation below:

$$CO_2 + H_2O \longrightarrow H_2CO_3$$

$$\text{Carbon dioxide + Water} \longrightarrow \text{Carbonic Acid}$$

The time it takes for the color to change is an indication for how quickly respiration is taking place (rate of respiration).

Materials

Germinating seeds	Cotton Balls	Non-Germinating Seeds
2 Test Tubes	2 Rubber Stoppers	Test Tube Rack
Bromothymol blue	Tape	Water

Procedure

A. To each test tube add 30ml of water (about 2cm) and 5 drops of Bromthymol blue and a loose cotton ball.

B. To one test tube add a few germinating seeds. To the other test tube add some non-germinating seeds.

C. Seal closed each test tube with a rubber stopper and record the time on your data table. Use the illustration as a guide for your test tube set up.

D. Observe the test tubes and record the time when you note a color change.

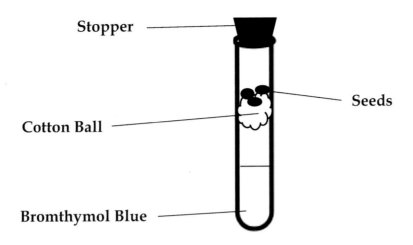

Stopper

Seeds

Cotton Ball

Bromthymol Blue

Data Table

Test Tube	Time Sealed	Time Color Changed	Elapsed Time

Analysis and Conclusion

1-What color change does the Bromthymol blue undergo in the presence of dissolved CO_2?

_____

2-How does the pH of the water change as CO_2 dissolves in it? (increase, decrease)

_____

3-What is the purpose of using the non-germinating seeds?

_____

_____

4-From your class observations, or data, what evidence is there that the germinating seeds are performing respiration?

_____

_____

5-Why was cotton, and not a tight-fitting piece of plastic tubing, used to support the seeds in the test tubes?

_____

_____

6-Based on your results, what would you expect to happen to the concentration of O_2 in the test tube?

_____

_____

7-In terms of diffusion, explain what is happening to the oxygen and carbon dioxide gases. Be sure to mention the seed root cells.

_____

_____

_____

8-What would happen to the respiration rate in the germinating seeds if the test tube was kept sealed for several days?

_____

_____

9-Suppose you repeat this experiment using an equivalent amount of living animal tissue from another organism; you find the indicator changed color more quickly than it did with the germinating seeds. Explain and compare the respiration rates of these two samples.

_____

_____

_____

Further Understanding

A sprig (stem with leaves) of a nettle plant was put in a jar of air fouled by breathing, as to extinguish a candle. It was placed in a room and left overnight. The next morning the air was found to be as bad as before. At 9 o'clock the morning, the jar was put in the sunshine, and in the space of two hours, was so much more corrected, that it was found to be nearly as good as common air.

10-The "jar full of air fouled by breathing" probably contained an excess of what gas?

_____

11-The fact that "the air was found to be as bad as before" was due to a process taking place in the plant, which also takes place in animals. Name that process.

_____

12-Which process did the plants perform to produce air nearly as good as "common air"?

_____

13-Name the gas produced by the plant in the process that improved the air in the jar.

_____

14-Name the gas that was produced by the plant in the dark.

_____

Chromatography

Materials: Chromatography strips with holes punched or squares, straws, beakers, toothpicks, water soluble markers, chlorophyll concentrate or leaves from 4 different plants (labeled A, B, C, and D), and scissors. (If working with plant leaves, 4 coins will also be needed)

In this lab you will create chromatograms using chlorophyll from 4 different plants. You will describe the visible pigments that appear after the chromatograms have dried.

In the science of paper chromatography, a mixture of substances in a suitable solvent is allowed to move up (or down) a paper strip by capillary action. During the movement, the substances become separated into individual bands.

The principle of chromatography is based upon two characteristics of the materials being separated: their attraction for the absorbent (in this case the fibers in the paper) and their ability to dissolve (solubility) in the solvent (in this case water). Those materials that have the greatest attraction for the paper fibers and/or are the least able to dissolve in water will move slowly and will be left behind; those substances that are not as attracted to the paper will move quickly and accumulate near the first water molecules that pass along the paper.

Chromatography is an especially useful technique for separating small quantities of substances which occur in mixtures. It can also be used to check for the presence or absence of chemicals in small amounts of plant tissue.

1- Unlike substances that have been chemically combined, substances in a mixture can be separated. Chromatography is a technique where substances in a mixture can be separated into individual _____.

2-What are the two characteristics of the materials that chromatography is based on?

   A)_____

   _____

   B)_____

   _____

3-During the technique of chromatography, substances that are less soluble (able to dissolve in water) will

_____

4-During the technique of chromatography, substances that are more soluble (able to dissolve in water) will

_____

5-In this lab, what will we be using as a solvent?

_____

6-What is chromatography useful for?

_____

_____

Procedure:

A) Obtain 2 beakers, 2 straws, 4 chromatography strips (or 1 beaker and a chromatography square), and 4 toothpicks. Be sure that the chromatography paper is the same length. Trim as necessary.

B) Place a PENCIL line 1 cm across the chromatography paper (each of the strips OR the square).

C) If you are working with chlorophyll concentrate, use a separate toothpick to apply a SMALL VERY DARK DOT of chlorophyll on the pencil line for each of the 4 plants. Use more chlorophyll to make dot as dark as possible, while still keeping it small. Label the dots A, B, C, and D as indicated. (If you are working with plant leaves, use a separate coin to rub the chlorophyll from each leaf on each of the chromatography strips or on the appropriate section of the chromatography square).

D) The smaller and darker your chlorophyll dots, the better your results will be. When your dots are dark enough—
    Slide your 2 chromatography strips, spaced far apart, onto a straw and place them in a beaker.

    OR

    Fold your chromatography square in half lengthwise and stand up in a beaker.

E) Place just enough water in the beaker to touch the only the very bottom of the chromatography paper (strips or square).

Two Possible Experimental Setups

4 Chromatography Strips

Chromatography Square

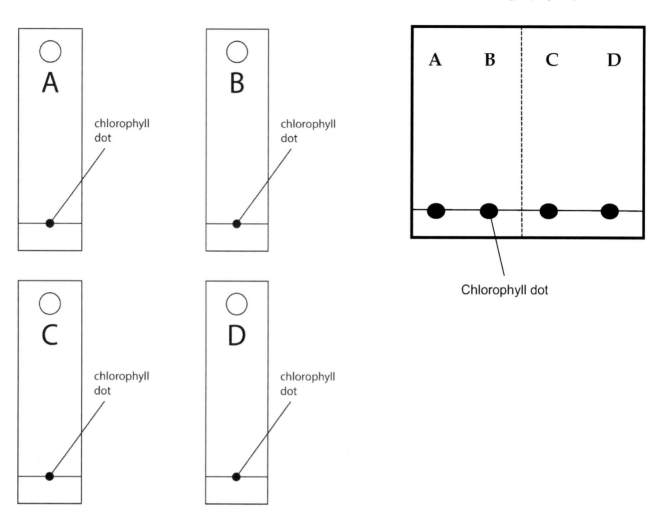

chlorophyll dot (A)

chlorophyll dot (B)

chlorophyll dot (C)

chlorophyll dot (D)

A B C D

Chlorophyll dot

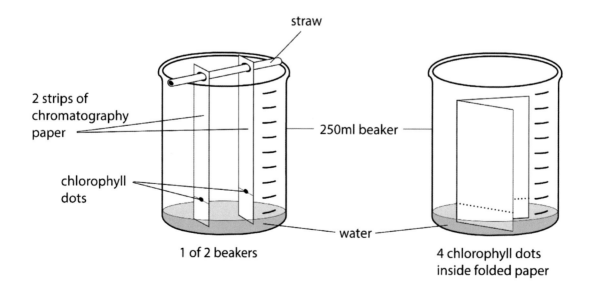

straw

2 strips of chromatography paper

250ml beaker

chlorophyll dots

water

1 of 2 beakers

4 chlorophyll dots inside folded paper

7-Why use a separate toothpick for each of the chlorophyll extract samples?

_____

_____

F) Once the water has moved up the paper, remove it from the beaker.

G) Use colored pencils to record the results of your chromatograms below. Be sure to label the colored bands:

CAROTENES----------------Orange colored bands

XANTHOPHYLLS-----------Yellow colored bands

CHLOROPHYLL A----------Blue-green bands

CHLOROPHYLL B----------Yellow-green bands

A	B	C	D

A   B   C   D

8- Explain the results of your chlorophyll chromatograms in terms of pigments found in leaves.

_____

_____

_____

9- What plants seem most closely related (A, B, C, D)?

_____

10- What plants seem least closely related (A, B, C, D)?

_____

11- On what do you base your opinion for numbers 9 and 10 above?

_____

_____

_____

H) Obtain 2 different colors of water-soluble markers. Complete chromatograms for the markers using the same procedures you used with the chlorophyll. Color and label your results below.

Marker Color: _____

Pigments: _____

_____

_____

Marker Color: _____

Pigments: _____

_____

_____

12a) Marker Color _____ resulted in a separation of the following pigments:

_____

12b) Marker Color _____ resulted in a separation of the following pigments:

_____

Fermentation in Yeast

Yeasts and few other microorganisms use alcoholic fermentation to release energy from food molecules. This is an anaerobic process.

During alcoholic fermentation NADH is converted back to the high-energy electron carrier NAD^+, thus allowing glycolysis to continue producing a steady supply of ATP.

When yeast runs out of oxygen, it begins to ferment. In addition to the production of NAD^+, alcoholic fermentation gives off bubbles of
1-_____ and alcohol as byproducts. (When yeast is mixed with flour to make bread dough, these bubbles cause bread to rise, as well as the spaces you see in the bread. The small amount of alcohol evaporates during baking.)

In this activity, we will ATTEMPT to show that yeast gives off carbon dioxide during fermentation.

Class Observation:

Place Bromthymol Blue in a test tube. Breathe into the test tube. Observe color change.

2- Bromthymol Blue is an indicator for _____. When we exhaled into a test tube with Bromthymol Blue indicator, the indicator changed from blue to _____ in _____ seconds.

Materials (quantities per lab group):

1 package of yeast	1 covered container large enough to fit yeast and small medicine dispenser cup
1 packet/tsp sugar	1 small medicine dispenser cup
water	1 pipette Bromthymol Blue
1 pipette	Stirring utensil

Setup/Procedure:

A. Open the package of yeast and place the contents close to the "wall" of the large container. Moisten yeast with water, adding only 1 pipette at a time and then stirring.

B. Add packet of sugar and mix. Keep the mixture in a small area near the "wall" of the container. **The yeast, water, and sugar should form a PASTE. Add tiny amounts of water so that your mixture does not become too runny!!**

C. Obtain a pipette of Bromthymol Blue in a small cup. Place this next to, but not on the yeast mixture. Cover the large container. Label it with the names of the people in your lab group. Put it in a warm place.

D. Wait. Stuff takes time.

Analysis (Answer questions in complete sentences on separate, lined paper):

3-Why was sugar added to the yeast?

4-Why not add flour instead of sugar?

5-Why did we put the container in a warm place?

6-Did the indicator change color?

7-If the indicator changed color, what does this prove? If the indicator did not change color, what might be a possible reason?

8-What is the difference between aerobic and anaerobic processes?

9-What is the other kind of fermentation? (see Dragonfly text 225 (Miller and Levine))

10-Explain how the process in #9 works.

Observing Photosynthesis

Plants need three basic things to live: water, sunlight, and carbon dioxide. The process of taking these three key ingredients and making them into food is called photosynthesis. Plants absorb carbon dioxide and release oxygen. They are the major source of oxygen on planet Earth and help keep us alive.

Plants capture sunlight using a compound called chlorophyll. Chlorophyll is green, which is why so many plants appear green. You might think that plants are green because they want to absorb and use green light. That is incorrect! In fact, scientists know that the color we see is the color of light that is reflected. So, chlorophyll reflects green light and absorbs blue and red light. Chlorophyll is found inside plant's cells in structures called chloroplasts.

There are two main phases to the process of photosynthesis. In the first phase, sunlight is captured by the chloroplasts and the energy is stored in a chemical called ATP. In the second phase, the ATP is used to create sugar and organic compounds. These are the foods plants use to live and grow.

The first phase of the process must have sunlight, but the second phase can happen without sunlight and even at night. The second phase is called the Calvin Cycle because it was discovered and described by scientist Melvin Calvin.

Even though plants need sunlight and water to live, different plants need different amounts of each. Some plants need just a little water while others need a lot. Some plants like to be in the direct sunlight all day, while others prefer the shade. Learning about the needs of plants can help you learn where to plant them in your yard and how best to water them, so they will flourish.

1-What three things do plants need to live?

_____

_____

_____

2-What is photosynthesis?

_____

_____

3-What compound enables plants to capture light?

_____

4-Why do plants appear green?

_____

_____

5-The first phase of photosynthesis results in energy being stored in

_____

6-In the second phase of photosynthesis, ATP helps the plant make

_____

7-Why do you think the second phase of photosynthesis is sometimes called the dark cycle?

_____

_____

Complete the following activity using Bromothymol blue and a sprig of elodea.

A. Place 1 ml of Bromothymol Blue (BTB) in a beaker of 30 ml of water. Observe the color change to blue. This is an oxygen rich/carbon dioxide poor solution.

B. Place 10 ml of that solution in a test tube (1) and cover it. It will be a control.

C. With a straw, blow into the beaker of BTB solution. See the color change from blue to yellow/green. This is an oxygen poor/carbon dioxide rich solution.

D. Place 10 ml of that solution in a test tube (2) and cover it. It, too, will be a control.

E. Place an elodea sprig in a third test tube (3), stem side down. Place 10 ml of the yellow/green solution from the beaker into that same test tube and cover it.

F. Place all three test tubes in a sunlit area for 24 hours.

G. After 24 hours, observe that the two controls remain unchanged: Test tube 1 stayed blue; test tube 2 stayed yellow/green.

H. Observe, also, that the solution in the 3rd test tube, with the elodea sprig, changed from yellow/green to green/greenish blue.

8-What is the purpose of this experiment?

_____

_____

_____

_____

_____

_____

9-The first controlled variable/test tube setup is BTB solution. It has a _____ tint.

10-How was CO_2 added to the BTB in the beaker? _____

11- BTB is an indicator for the presence of CO_2. What color does BTB change to in the presence of CO_2?

_____

12-The second controlled variable/test tube setup is BTB + ?

_____

The third test tube was the experimental variable. In it, a sprig of elodea had been placed in BTB. The BTB was greenish-yellow because carbon dioxide had been added to it. After 24 hours in front of the heat lamp, the liquid with the elodea was less yellow.

13-What color is the liquid in the third test tube with the elodea sprig after 24 hours?

_____

14-Since the color is no longer greenish-yellow and has now turned back to green, there must be less of what gas in the liquid?

_____

15-Predict what the color of the liquid in the test tube with the elodea sprig might change to if it sat for another 24 hours in front of the heat lamp.

_____

16-Diagram the Carbon Dioxide – Oxygen Cycle using the illustrations provided. Explain the cycle below. (Illustrations are not to scale).

_____

_____

_____

_____

_____

_____

_____

_____

_____

_____

_____

_____

_____

_____

_____

Classification

Classifying Animals

Every known organism is classified and named by a set of rules. Those rules are used by all scientists. The scientific name given to an organism is different than its common name. Common names are the ones you might use when talking with your friends. "Dog" is an example of a common name for the organisms with the scientific name *Canis familiarus*.

Scientists use a two-name system called Binomial Nomenclature. The two names refer to an organism's genus and species. The first word (its genus) is capitalized; the second word (its species) is not. Humans are scientifically named *Homo sapiens*. You may also see an abbreviation of this name as *H. sapiens* where the genus is only represented by the first letter.

1-What is the scientific two-name system called?

_____

2-What is special about how genus and species need to be written?

_____

_____

Carolus Linnaeus began the naming system (called taxonomy), which is based on similarities between different organisms. He also chose to use Latin words for naming organisms.

The system of taxonomy used to group animals and plants by characteristics and relationships. Previously, scientists looked at the shared characteristics (traits) that organisms had in common. They then used the shared characteristics to determine their common ancestry.

For example, scientists would group all creatures that had a nose together because of that shared trait. That method has changed because of scientist's greater understanding of DNA. Organisms are now organized by a combination of observable traits and genetics, not one superficial trait (like a nose).

3-How has the classification of organisms changed with greater scientific understanding?

_____

_____

_____

_____

The taxonomic system has different levels (or taxons). The most general taxon is KINGDOM. Kingdoms have many, many organisms that share a couple of characteristics. The next taxon is PHYLUM, then CLASS, ORDER, FAMILY, GENUS, and finally, SPECIES, which is very specific. There can only be one type of organism in each species taxon.

4-Write the taxons from most general (least specific) to least general (most specific):

_____

_____

_____

_____

_____

_____

_____

As scientists have expanded their knowledge about life, they added to Linnaeus' classification system. We now have a grouping over the kingdom level called DOMAIN. There are three domains used in modern classification. The domain EUKARYA is used for all eukaryotic species that include protists, fungi, plants, and animals. The two domains BACTERIA and ARCHEA are used to group two different types of prokaryote (non-nucleoid) organisms. They are in different domains because of differences on a molecular level.

In order to better understand how classification works, let's use the example of how humans are grouped in the taxonomic system:

A) Because human cells have nuclei, we are in the EUKARYA domain.

B) Since we are multicellular, and our cells do not have cell walls or chloroplasts, we are in the ANIMALIA kingdom.

C) Our vertebrae developed from a cartilaginous rod (called a notochord) when we were developing in our mother's womb. That makes part of the CHORDATA phylum.

D) Humans can regulate their body temperature, have hair on their bodies, develop in a womb with a placenta, and can breast-feed their young. That makes us part of the MAMMALIA class.

E) We have five-fingered hands that can grasp, with flat fingernails. We also have collarbones. That puts us in the PRIMATA order, along with monkeys.

F) We diverge from monkeys because we lack a tail, walk on two legs (bipedalism), and have an "S" shaped spinal cord. We are in the HOMINIDAE family.

G) Getting more specific now, we are in the HOMO genus. Compared to earlier bi-pedal walkers, we have a large cranial capacity, a habitual erect posture and bipedal gait, well-developed and fully opposable thumbs, hands capable of power and precision grips, and the ability to make standardized precision tools, using one tool to make another.

H) Finally, at the species level, we are SAPIENS, different from other human-like ancestors that came before us. SAPIENS demonstrated the ability to use new technology and abstract symbols to achieve goals.

5-List the taxonomic categories for humans from most general (least specific) to least general (most specific). Some are done for you.

Eukarya

_____

_____

_____

_____

_____

_____

sapiens

Now you will have an opportunity to classify some organisms. Like humans, these organisms are in the Eukarya Domain and the Animal Kingdom. That is where their similarities end. These animals belong to several different phyla. Your job will be to:

- Spread your set of 21 Animal Cards out on the table.
- Look at each of the Animal Cards, noting similarities and differences among the animals.
- Read the information on each card. This information represents what you might discover if you observed the actual animals more closely and were able to dissect a specimen.
- Classify the animals into 5-8 groups representing the phylum level. Work together to agree on a classification system.
- In the table below, describe the groups that you created. Note: The number of rows in your table will depend on the number of groups you created.

6-

GROUP	WHICH ANIMALS ARE IN THIS GROUP? (NUMBERS)	WHAT DO THE ANIMALS IN EACH GROUP HAVE IN COMMON?

After you have completed classifying your animal cards and written your answers in the table above, obtain the **Scientist's Classification Sheet** from your instructor. This is how taxonomists have classified these same animals. **Each phylum contains 3 animal cards. Write the number of the 3 animal cards that belong to each phylum. Staple your completed sheet to the back of your lab.**

19.

The underside of this land animal is flat. It has an elongated body. It consumes other invertebrates. It does not have a respiratory system. Oxygen is absorbed directly through its skin into its bodies' cells. This mechanism is known as cutaneous respiration, skin breathing, or diffusion.

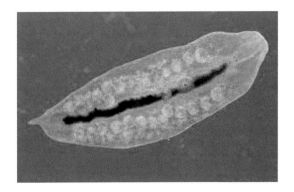

2.

This animal is an unsegmented, soft-bodied invertebrate. It has no specialized circulatory or respiratory organs. Its flat body allows oxygen and nutrients to pass through by diffusion. Its digestive cavity has only one opening for both ingestion and egestion.

5.

This is a medium-sized, flat terrestrial animal. It feeds on other soft-bodied animals. It is moist and absorbs oxygen through its skin. It preys upon other soft-bodied animals.

20.

This invertebrate lives in a mucous tube for protection. The animal shows only its tentacles to feed, usually at nighttime. It has a single body cavity for digestion and respiration. The animal can retract itself inside the tube for resting or if it feels any danger.

3.

This animal is a filter feeder. Its tentacles catch plankton drifting past on the current. It protects itself from predators with its unpleasant taste. Water flowing through its tissues also provides it with oxygen and removes its waste products.

4.

This segmented animal burrows into the mud. It ingests tiny dead plants and animals in the soil. As it does so, it ingests soil, as well. Air dissolves on the mucus of its skin. These animals MUST stay moist to breathe. Once oxygen is drawn into its circulatory system the heart pumps it throughout its body.

7.

Algae live within this animal and provide it with some nourishment. It also catches tiny floating animals called zooplankton. Its singing cells help it to obtain food. Gases are exchanged through its cells that are in contact with its watery environment.

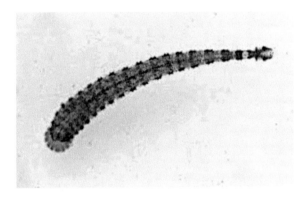

12.

This animal is found in differing types of running and stagnant waters. It is usually on leaves or sticks that float on the water surface. It feeds on the blood of different fish and amphibians. The animal has body segments that help to enhance its uptake of oxygen through its cells.

9.

This animal lives in the ocean and feeds off particles left by coral. Its front-most segment has two eyes and five antennae, the next segment is very long, and the remaining segments have legs and bristles. Gasses pass through its skin through diffusion.

10.

This animal uses its venom to paralyze small crustaceans before it eats them. It uses gills for oxygen uptake but may also absorb oxygen through its skin for short periods. Its soft body consists of a head (mantle) that contains all its internal organs, and tentacles which help it with hunting and propulsion.

17.

This is an air-breathing, terrestrial, carnivorous animal. It has a soft body that is essentially a foot—for locomotion. It also has a shell to house and protect its organs.

14.

This animal feeds primarily on algae. It can live out of water for a short time. Gas exchange occurs when submerged, as water flows over it. It has separate shell plates which overlap to provide protection and locomotion. It is also able to creep along rocks with a muscular foot.

11.

With an exoskeleton and jointed legs, this tiny animal is a menace. It is a parasite that afflicts honeybees. This creature feeds on the bee's blood.

8.

This animal has eight jointed legs and two pedipalps. Its tail has a venom-injecting barb. Instead of bones, the animal has an exoskeleton made of chitin, which is similar to the shell of a shrimp.

15.

Iridescent wings are found on some members of this species. It has a four-stage life cycle in which immature stages are very different from the adult. Its body is segmented, it is protected by an exoskeleton, and it has jointed legs.

16.

This is a short-limbed animal with a small, conical skull and a long, heavily furred tail. Its tail is an extension of its vertebral column. It has a complex nervous and circulatory system. It has two highly developed scent glands on each side of the anus.

13.

This animal is arboreal. It has large toe pads which allow it to grip well on branches. The animal has a complex nervous system. It has a very short vertebral column. The pelvis is a single vertebra with connected legbones. The legbones are stout and specialized for jumping. Its circulatory system is well developed.

18.

Found in oceans, this animal feeds on encrusting sponges, detritus or small invertebrates. The organization of its body shows radiation from a central disc. Its body developed from three embryonic cell layers (ectoderm, mesoderm, and endoderm).

6.

This animal is long tailed with a short, thick bill and prominent crest. It often sits with a hunched-over posture and its tail pointed straight down. The animal's circulatory system is well developed. It has a complex nervous system. Its flexible neck vertebrae allow it to groom its feathers.

21.

This animal is found on the seabed in shallow water on reef flats, in lagoons and estuaries. Its body is flexible and elongated with radial symmetry. Its cylindrical design formed in layers during embryonic development.

48

1.

Found in shallow ocean waters, young among these species conceal themselves in crevices and under rocks during the day but adults stay in the open ocean. This animal has a spherical body with parts radiating out from its central axis. As an embryo, cell division produces the three germ layers which are instrumental in the development of the adult.

Scientist's Classification Sheet

GROUP	WHICH ANIMALS ARE IN THIS GROUP? (NUMBERS)	WHAT DO THE ANIMALS IN EACH GROUP HAVE IN COMMON?
Platyhelminthes		• Flat worm • Gases move through skin through diffusion • Soft body
Cnidaria		• Tentacles/stinging cells • Water moves through body • Oxygen/food flow with water though tissues
Annelida		• Segmented • Oxygen moves through skin/diffusion • Needs water/moisture
Mollusca		• Soft body • Uses foot to move
Arthropoda		• Exoskeleton • Jointed legs
Chordata		• Vertebrae • Complex nervous and circulatory system
Echioderm		• Radial symmetry • Marine dwelling • Three germ layers

7-Describe how closely your animal cards matched how the taxonomists classified them? What number cards did you group together as taxonomists did?

_____

_____

_____

8-Why might biologist have classified the animals differently than you did?

_____

_____

Dichotomous Keys

Introduction

In this lab, you will first use a dichotomous key to identify sharks. A dichotomous key is built around pairs of contradictory (opposing or dichotomous) statements that describe a visible trait. The reader of a dichotomous key must select the statement in each pair that best describes an organism. By following the steps in the key, the reader narrows down the list of choices and finally names the organism. After you have practiced using a dichotomous key, you will design your own key for a group of organisms.

During this lab, you will need to observe, classify, compare, contrast, and sequence

Procedure

Part A: Use a Dichotomous Key

Before you try to identify sharks, you need to understand a bit about shark anatomy. Figure 1 is a general shark drawing with labels showing the possible locations of fins. Refer to Figure 1 as you use the dichotomous key to identify the sharks labeled A through F.

Figure 1 General external anatomy of shark

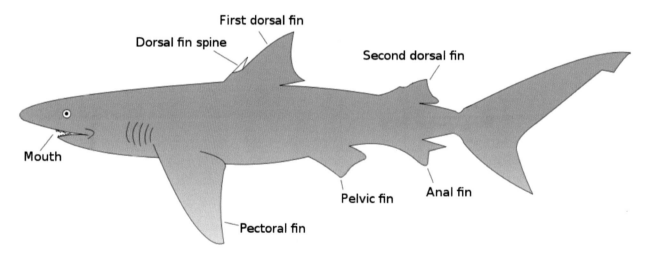

1-According to the general anatomical drawing of the shark in figure 1, what are three different physical traits that can be used to identify sharks in a dichotomous key?

_____

_____

_____

_____

Dichotomous Key for Sharks

Step	Characteristic	Species
1a	Anal fin present . . . *Go to Step 2*	
1b	No anal fin . . . *Go to Step 6*	
2a	One dorsal fin	*Notorynchus cepedianus,* Sevengill shark
2b	Two dorsal fins . . . *Go to Step 3*	
3a	Spines on dorsal fins	*Heterodontus francisci,* Horn shark
3b	No spines on dorsal fins . . . *Go to Step 4*	
4a	Mouth at front of head	*Rhincodon typus,* Whale shark
4b	Mouth at bottom of head . . . *Go to Step 5*	
5a	Eyes on ends of hammerlike projection	*Sphyrna zygaena,* Smooth hammerhead
5b	No hammerlike head....... *Go to Step 6*	
6a	Flattened body (like ray)	*Squatina squatina,* Angel shark
6b	Body not flattened . . . *Go to Step 7*	
7a	Pointed snout and powerful swimming fins	*Carcharodon carcharias,* Great white shark
7b	Small, slow swimming fins	*Somniosus microcephalus,* Greenland shark

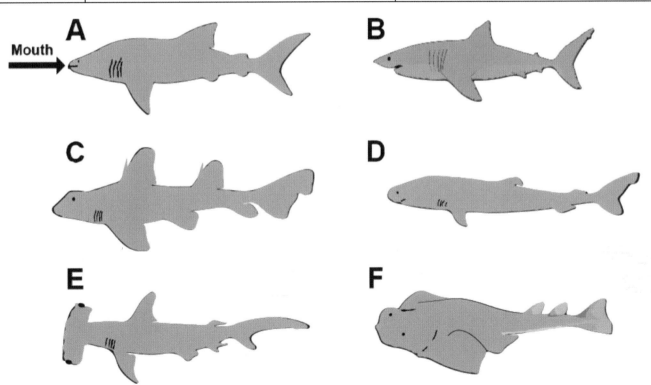

53

Shark	Scientific Name	Common Name
A		
B		
C		
D		
E		
F		

Part B: Construct a Dichotomous Key

Construct a dichotomous key for the insects pictured below. Use the key for sharks as a model. Start by choosing a trait that divides your organisms into two smaller groups. Keep dividing each of the smaller groups with pairs of statements until you have a final identifying statement for each of your species.

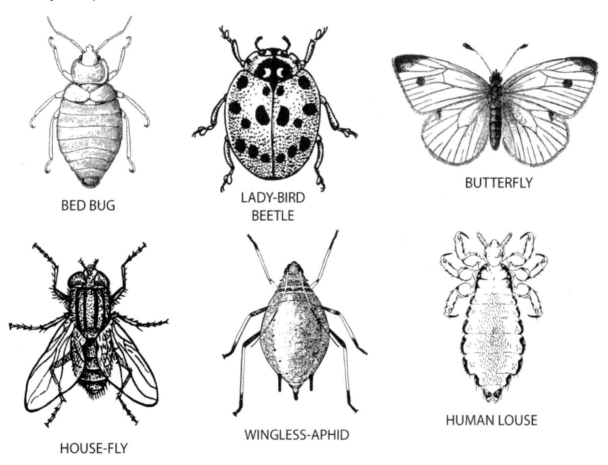

BED BUG

LADY-BIRD BEETLE

BUTTERFLY

HOUSE-FLY

WINGLESS-APHID

HUMAN LOUSE

3-Insect Dichotomous Key

_____

_____

_____

_____

_____

_____

_____

_____

_____

_____

_____

4-What other traits could you use to build a dichotomous key of insects if you had actual insects, rather than drawings?

_____

_____

_____

_____

5-A shark dichotomous key may group species of sharks that lack anal fins together. But a cladogram, a tool which shows relationships between species, indicates that the Greenland shark (without an anal fin) is actually more closely related to the Sevengill shark, which has an anal fin. Explain how a dichotomous key is different from a cladogram?

_____

_____

_____

_____

Silly Science Classification

A dichotomous key can be used to identify objects such as plants and minerals. The key on this page was designed to identify common objects. Discover the silly scientific name of each object. <u>You will need a metric ruler to do this activity!</u>

1a. Item is made of plastic....... Go to 2

1b. Item is not made of plastic...... Go to 6

2a. Item is completely one color.......................... Go to 3

2b. Item is not completely one color................. Cubey

3a. Item is not flexible............................ Go to 4

3b. Item is flexible............... Gumby

4a. The color of the item rhymes with "night" or "day" ......Go to 5

4b. The color of the item does not rhyme with "night" or "day" ......Mipsey

5a. The color of the item rhymes with "night" ......Flipsey

5b. The color of the item rhymes with "day" .... Dipsey

6a. The item is not made entirely of metal...... Go to 8

6b. The item is made entirely of metal......... Got to 7

7a. The item is more than 4 cm long....... Super Duper

7b. The item is less than 4 cm long...... Itsy Bitsy

8a. The item does not have any metal...... Go to 9

8b. The item contains some metal......Fuzzy

9a. The item is spherical....... Go to 10

9b. The item is not spherical ......Go to 11

10a. The item is clear or white.... Whatnot

10b. The item is not clear or white...... Fancy Whatnot

11a. The item is curved...... Go to 12

11b. The item is not curved...... Oopsey

12a. The item is cylindrical....... Go to 13

12b. The item is not cylindrical......... Gadget

13a. The item is white....... Screecher

13b. The item is not white...... Squealer

Object	Silly Scientific Name
A. White marble	_____
B. White Peg	_____
C. White Chalk	_____
D. Wooden Splint	_____
E. Grey Peg	_____
F. Colored marble	_____
G. Small Paperclip	_____
H. Eraser	_____
I. Die	_____
J. Large Paperclip	_____
K. Colored Chalk	_____
L. Pipe Cleaner	_____
M. Zip Tie	_____
N. Black Peg	_____

Understanding Taxonomy

There are currently eight levels of classification today: They are: Domain, Kingdom, Phylum, Class, Order, Family, Genus, and Species. (Linnaeus's original taxonomic system had seven levels. His system did not include the Domain level.) This addition is an example of the nature of science: Although reliable, science is tentative (open for re-consideration). Scientific knowledge can be modified when new evidence is found.

The top levels of the taxonomic system have the most organisms. There are fewer organisms as you go down the levels. By the time you get to the species level, there is only one kind of organism in the group.

1-What level of the taxonomic system has the most organisms?

_____

2-What level of the taxonomic system has the fewest organisms?

_____

Domain: This is the highest taxonomic rank of organisms which was developed by scientist Carl Woese in 1990. There are three domains: Archaea, Bacteria, and Eukarya. The archaea and bacteria domains are composed of microscopic prokaryotic organisms. Prokaryotic cells do not have nuclei. The domain eukarya contains organisms whose cells contain nuclei.

3-Although many scientists have contributed ideas to taxonomy, two scientists that have influenced the grouping of organisms have been mentioned in this lab. They are:

_____

_____

4-What is the main difference between eukaryotic and prokaryotic organisms?

_____

_____

Kingdom: Generally, scientists agree there are six kingdoms. Some scientists think that viruses should have their own kingdom, but currently they are not included under this system. The six kingdoms are: Archaebacteria, Eubacteria, Protista, Fungi, Plante, and Animalia.

For the purposes of this lab, we will now focus on the Kingdom Animalia

5-Why are animals grouped with eukaryotic organisms?

_____

_____

Phylum: Within the animal kingdom, animals are divided into more than 30 phyla (plural of "phylum"). For example, Phylum Chordata contains animals with backbones. Humans are in the phylum Chordata. (Note the word part "chord" in chordata is like spinal cord. Other phyla include porifera (sponges), annelida (segmented worms), and arthropodia (spiders, lobsters, centi- and milli-pedes, and insects).

Class: The fourth level of classification is class. For example, Phylum Chordata includes the classes aves (birds), reptiles, and mammals.

Order: Orders are smaller groups within the different classes. The Order Anseriformes includes ducks and geese, within the class aves.   The Order Crocodilia includes alligators and crocodiles, within the class reptile. Order Carnivora is within class mammalia which includes both cats and dogs.

Family: The sixth rank of classification is family. (Scientists sometimes disagree about which order or family an animal belongs to.) The order carnivora includes cats and dogs. Cats are in the Family Felidae; Dogs are in the Family Canidae.

Genus: Genus is the seventh rank. It may only have one or two species in it. If organisms are in the same genus, they are really closely related. In fact, you may not be able to tell them apart just by looking at them! When we write the name of the genus, we capitalize it and italicize it. For example, the genus of dogs (and wolves) is _Canis_.

Species: If two organisms can successfully breed (produce fertile offspring), they are a species. An organism's scientific name is its genus and species. We use a lowercase letter and italics for the species. The scientific name of dogs is _Canis familiaris_; the scientific name of wolves is _Canis lupus._

6-What parts of taxonomy are a species' scientific name?

_____

7-What are the important rules about how a scientific name is written?

_____

_____

Use the chart below to answer the questions that follow.

Common Name	Phylum	Class	Order	Family	Genus	Species
Horse	Chordata	Mammalia	Perissodactyla	Equidae	Equus	caballus
Wolf	Chordata	Mammalia	Carnivora	Canidae	Canis	lupus
Clown Fish	Chordata	Actinopterygii	Perciformes	Pomacentridaie	Amphiprion	ocellaris
Chilean Flamingo	Chordata	Aves	Ciconiiformes	Phoenicopteridae	Phoenicopterus	chilenis
Blue Whale	Chordata	Mammalia	Cetacea	Balaenopteridae	Balaenoptera	musculus
Dog	Chordata	Mammalia	Carnivora	Canidae	Canis	familiaris
Chimpanzee	Chordata	Mammalia	Primate	Pongidae	Pan	troglodyte
Housefly	Arthropoda	Insecta	Diptera	Muscidae	Musca	domestica
Cat	Chordata	Mammalia	Carnivora	Felidae	Felis	domesticus
Grasshopper	Arthropoda	Insecta	Orthoptera	Acrididae	Romalia	microptera
Lion	Chordata	Mammalia	Carnifora	Felidae	Panthera	leo

8-Listing the Kingdom of each of these organisms is unnecessary because they

_____

9-The Chilean flamingo is a bird, and, as such belongs to that class Aves, as do all birds. Airplane pilots are called aviators. Someone who studies to be a pilot goes to aviation school. Aves, aviator, and aviation are words having to do with _____

10-If two animals are the same genus, then they must also be the same family, order, class, phylum and kingdom, and domain: TRUE   or   FALSE

11-Explain your choice in #10 above.

_____

12-Horses belong to the Order Perissodactyla, meaning "odd toed." What any other animals (not on this chart) that might belong to the Order Perissodactyla?

_____

Re-read the sections labeled <u>Genus</u> and <u>Species</u> on the 2nd page of this lab, which explains how to write an organism's scientific name.

13-Write the scientific names for:

Blue whale- _____

Chimpanzee- _____

Housefly- _____

Sometimes the scientific name is abbreviated with the genus listed as a capital letter with a period after it, like this: *C. lupus*

14-Write the abbreviated scientific names for:

Blue whale- _____

Chimpanzee- _____

Housefly- _____

Go to Animal Diversity Web. Choose any animal you wish and list its classification taxons.

https://animaldiversity.org/

15-Animal you typed into the search: _____

Kingdom- _____

Phylum- _____

Class- _____

Order- _____

Family- _____

Genus- _____

Species- _____

Common Name Listed for this Species on ADW - _____

16-List two animals that might be very closely related to the animal you chose.

_____

_____

<u>Extra Credit/Extension (worth 12 points on lab):</u>

You are a researcher studying animals in the wild. One day, you see an animal you have never seen before. Back at camp, you research known animals and find that you have discovered a new species! As the discoverer of this new species, you get to name it. Following scientific conventions, this means the only part of the animal's name you will make up yourself is the species name.

Go to https://animaldiversity.org/

Find an animal that is very similar to the one you "discovered". For example, if the animal you have "discovered" a large cat, look up "panther" on the website.

Get a clear picture of the animal you "discovered" your mind. You could choose an animal that is similar, but slightly different, from the animal you chose on page three.

- <u>Draw a picture of the animal you "discovered" on a separate piece of unlined paper.</u> Make your animal slightly different from any other species in the genus. For example, it could be a different color, eat something different, or live in a different location. (4 points)
- <u>Label four characteristics about the animal in your drawing that are typical for that classification.</u> For example, backbone, egg laying, feathers, scales, exoskeleton, body segments, 3-pairs of legs, etc. (4 points)
- List the animal's classification taxons. All of the taxons should be the same as a very similar animal---except for species. (4 points)

Kingdom- _____

Phylum- _____

Class- _____

Order- _____

Family- _____

Genus- _____

Species- _____ - You make up the species name.

Ecology

Adapted for Survival? Bird Adaptations to Habitat

Part 1: Create a Bird & Its Habitat

Earth's vast array of life forms are the result of the diverse environments living things occupy. Adaptations are features that increase an organism's reproductive success (fitness) in its environment. Consider, for example, the effects of coloration, feeding mechanisms, and reproductive strategies on organisms' chances for survival. In this lab, you will investigate the effects of different bird adaptations in a range of habitats.

Create a Bird Instructions

1-Read the description of your habitat and draw the habitat on a large piece of unlined paper, showing details such as plants, animals, water, soil, etc. IN COLOR. **LABEL THE TYPE OF HABITAT ON YOUR DRAWING** (found on the description card). Write your name on the back of your habitat drawing.

2-Design a bird to live in this habitat.

   a-Choose one of each type of beak, feet, and nest, using the "Create a Bird" page.

   b-Create a SPECIFIC COMMON NAME (SCN) by pairing your own idea with a bird type. Examples of bird types are: crane, finch, jay, vulture, warbler, thrush, lark, hawk, and gull. Examples of specific common names (SCN): Francine's Vulture / Christina's Lark.

   b-Title a lined piece of paper BIRD ADAPTATIONS OF SCN. Write your name above the title. Then list and describe your bird's specific adaptations. For example:

   1. Francine's Vulture eats by   _____

   2. Christina's Lark gets its food by   _____

   3. SCN builds its nest by   _____

   4. SCN chooses a mate by   _____

   5. SCN raises its young by   _____

   6. SCN protects itself from predators by   _____

   7. SCN is adapted to survive in its specific habitat because   _____

3-Using a smaller piece of unlined paper design, color and **cut out** one bird showing all the adaptations you have chosen and described. Use your imagination to add details!

4-Write your name on the back of your bird. <u>Paperclip</u> it to your habitat. Submit your bird, habitat, and Bird Adaptations of SCN page.

Create a Bird	
A-Choose a habitat	D-Choose a nesting strategy. (Circle)
B-Choose a beak. (Circle)	E-Draw your bird.
C-Choose a foot type. (Circle)	F-Place it in its habitat.

Adapted for Survival? Bird Adaptations to Habitat

Part 2: Bird Species in New Habitat

Your instructor has re-arranged the birds and habitats from Part 1 of this activity.

Respond to the following:

1-My bird, _____, was adapted to a _____

habitat. It now lives in a _____ habitat.

2-What adaptations will limit the success of your bird in the new habitat

_____

_____

3-Why do you think so?

_____

_____

4-What adaptations will enhance the success of your bird in the new habitat

_____

_____

5-Why do you think so?

_____

_____

6-Which adaptation is most important to the survival of the individual bird?

_____

_____

7-Why?

_____

_____

8-Which adaptation is most important to the survival of your bird's species

_____

_____

9-Why?

_____

_____

10-If my bird's species is not well adapted to its new environment it will not s_____

long enough to r_____ and pass its genes onto its o_____.

This is called Natural S_____.

Habitat Description Cards

1-Salt Marsh: Salt marshes are wetlands found at the edges of bays and estuaries. The tide carries salty water in and out of the marsh. Low-growing plants grow here. Plankton and fish live in the water, crabs and clams burrow in the mud, and mice and insects live in the plants.

2-Redwood Forest: Redwood forests exist where fog creates a moist environment. Tall red-woods form a dense canopy that shades the forest floor. Ferns, moss, and fungus grow in the understory and redwood needles form a soft blanket of duff on the ground. Squirrels, slugs, and deer live in the forest.

3-Grasslands: These are low-lying flat areas are covered with grasses. Lizards and snakes bake on exposed rocks. Kit foxes and kangaroo rats roam during the night. Summers are hot and winters are cold.

4-Mountains/Alpine: These are high elevations which are inhabited by pine trees and aspens. Snow falls through the winter and melts in the spring, running down creeks to rivers. The air is crisp and cold.

5-Desert: Most deserts are arid regions that are typically hot during the day and cool at night. Very little rain falls, and all of the plants and animals have to find ways to conserve water and tolerate the heat.

6-Riparian: Riparian areas are located along-side rivers and streams. Various trees grow here. A wide variety of animals seek shelter, food, and water in these shady areas. The river water flows over rocks and sandy areas inhabited by invertebrates and fish.

7-Beach/Shoreline: Sandy shore is where ocean meets land. Invertebrates live in the sand. Dead bits of kelp and animals are washed up with the tides each day. Decomposers work at drift kelp lying on sand. Sand dunes form at highest points on beach, and beach grasses and flowering plants grow.

Teacher instructions-
- Assign each student or pair (if working in teams) a habitat. (Cut out habitat description cards and give to students)
- Students will design their bird based upon their habitat.
- It may be helpful to supplement habitat descriptions with photographs.

Calculating Exponential Growth

Scenario:

1-Suppose that one mated (M/F) pair of rabbits in a park can produce a litter of six offspring each year. Each generation generally produces approximately 50% of each gender, so assume that there are equal numbers of males and females in each generation. Further assume that each pair of rabbits breeds only once, and no offspring die. Calculate <u>how many offspring</u> would be produced each year for five generations. Show all calculations below:

YEAR 1:

YEAR 2:

YEAR 3:

YEAR 4:

YEAR 5:

Thinking About Populations:

2-Construct a graph of your data. Plot and label Time on the X-axis. Plot and label Number of Offspring on the Y-axis. Title the graph.

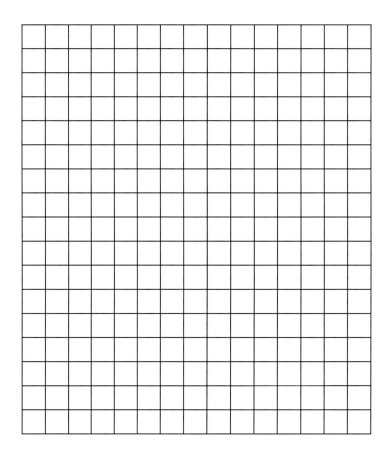

Describe the shape of the five-generation rabbit population graph you constructed above.

_____

_____

_____

_____

Predict:

3-In fact, if the rabbit population continued its current trend (the number of couples tripling each year: 9, 27, 81, 243), the ten-year number of offspring could be calculated mathematically as follows:

$$2 \times 3^{10} = 2 \times 59{,}049$$

Complete the calculation:

$$
\begin{array}{r}
59{,}049 \\
\times \quad\quad\quad 2 \\
\hline
\end{array}
$$

And, the twenty-year number of offspring could similarly be calculated mathematically as follows:

$$2 \times 3^{20} = 2 \times 3{,}486{,}784{,}401$$

Complete the calculation:

$$
\begin{array}{r}
3{,}486{,}784{,}401 \\
\times \quad\quad\quad 2 \\
\hline
\end{array}
$$

4-Construct a new graph. This time, Plot and label Time <u>for twenty years</u> on the X-axis. Plot and label Number of Offspring <u>for ten billion</u> on the Y-axis. Title the graph.

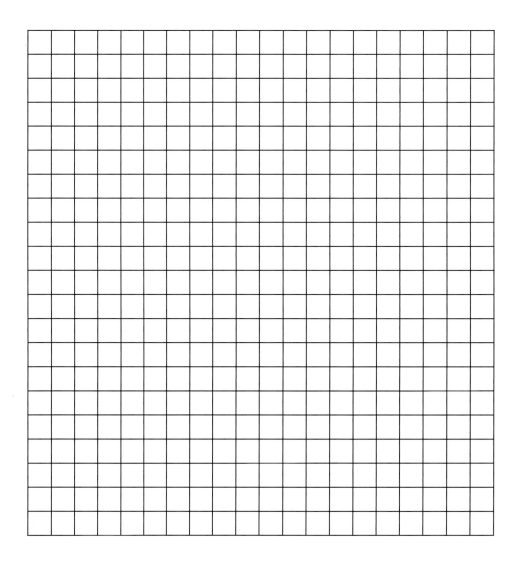

A) What would eventually happen to the population of rabbits if they were not able to leave the park?

_____

_____

B) How can you explain the fact that Earth is not covered by rabbits?

_____

_____

Name_____ Date_____ Period_____ Lab_____

Predator-Prey Relationships

Predator organisms feed upon other organisms, called prey. The predators depend on and limit the population of prey organisms.   In other words, the size of the predator and prey populations are dependent upon each other. In this exercise, we will examine the relationship between two animals found in Arizona. The prey species is the jackrabbit (a primary consumer) and the predator species is the coyote (a secondary consumer). A study was done over a period of twenty-five years to track the populations of both the jackrabbits and coyotes in a five square kilometer area south of Prescott. The data is listed in the table below:

Year	Jackrabbits per square kilometer	Coyotes per 5 square kilometers
1979	60	5
1980	75	5
1981	80	15
1982	89	20
1983	79	22
1984	72	18
1985	53	8
1986	45	4
1987	57	6
1988	65	8
1989	87	15
1990	90	16
1991	90	17
1992	89	20
1993	79	22
1994	72	18
1995	53	8
1996	45	4
1997	57	6
1998	65	8
1999	87	15
2000	90	16
2001	90	17
2002	93	20
2003	95	22

STEPS:

1. On the top of the graph paper, give the graph a TITLE that describes what the graph represents.

2. Label the x-axis YEARS and the y-axis NUMBER OF ANIMALS.

3. Start with zero on the corner of the y-axis and create a scale counting every other line with multiples of 5 (5, 10, 15, 20…)

4. Create a scale on the x-axis with the years, beginning with 1979. Do not skip lines.

5. Plot the data from the table above, using an "o" for coyotes and an "x" for jackrabbits.

6. Connect all the "o" dots to each other and all the "x" dots to each other, to show two separate lines on the graph.

7. Make a key on the graph showing the "o" for coyotes and "x" for jackrabbits.

ANSWER THE FOLLOWING SUMMARY QUESTIONS

1-What do you notice about the coyote and jackrabbit data points/lines?

_____

_____

_____

_____

_____

2-Why do you think this type of graph is called cyclic?

_____

_____

_____

_____

_____

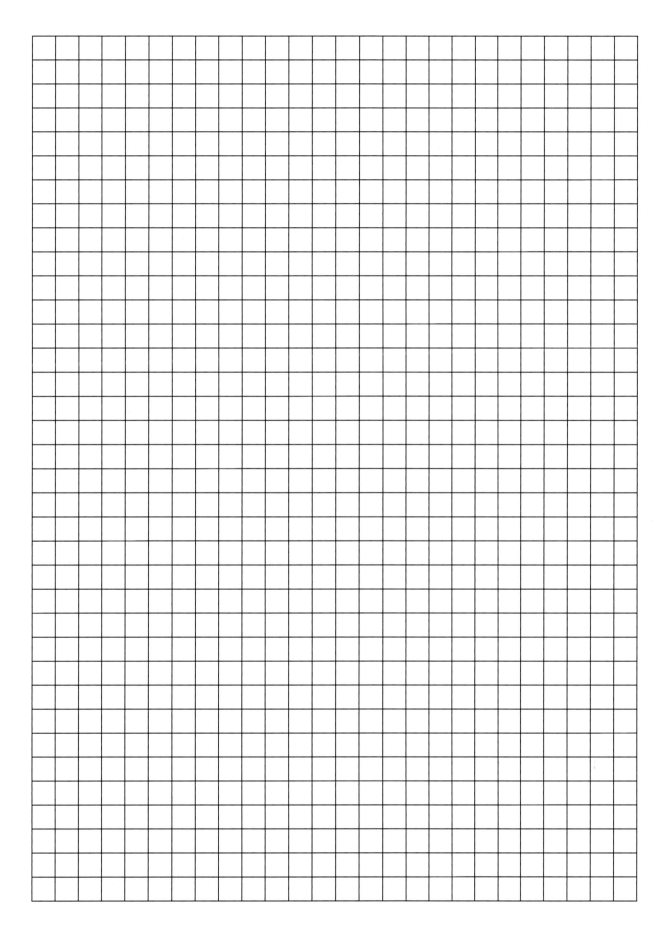

Studying Population Growth

A population growth curve generally shows four phases. When a population is becoming established in a new environment, the growth curve shows a LAG PHASE, during which the organisms adjust to the new environment, and the population shows little increase in numbers. If nutrients are available and environmental conditions favorable, the organisms begin to reproduce at a much higher rate than they are dying off. This stage is known as the EXPONENTIAL PHASE. When the population reaches a certain size, the available resources are only enough to maintain the number of organisms present. The population then enters a STATIONARY PHASE, in which the birth-rate and death-rate are equal, and the population number remains constant. In some populations, there is a DEATH PHASE, where more organisms are dying than are being born, and the population decreases in numbers. This may occur because of the exhaustion of food supplies or accumulation of wastes.

Define each of the following phases of a population curve:

1-LAG PHASE- _____

2-EXPONENTIAL PHASE _____

3-STATIONARY PHASE _____

4-DEATH PHASE _____

5-What factors may contribute to a population entering a death phase?

_____

- The Model of Bacterial Growth Plates diagram shows a bacterial culture grown under optimal conditions in an incubator. Population counts were made at one-hour intervals.
- Record the population counts for each of the hour intervals on table 1.
- Graph the data from the table you completed. Put **Time in Hours** on the x-axis (horizontal) and **Population** on the y-axis (vertical). Title your graph **Bacterial Population Growth Curve.**
- Plot the data as follows:

- When the graph is completely plotted, label the phases from above on the graph.

Model of Bacterial Growth Plates

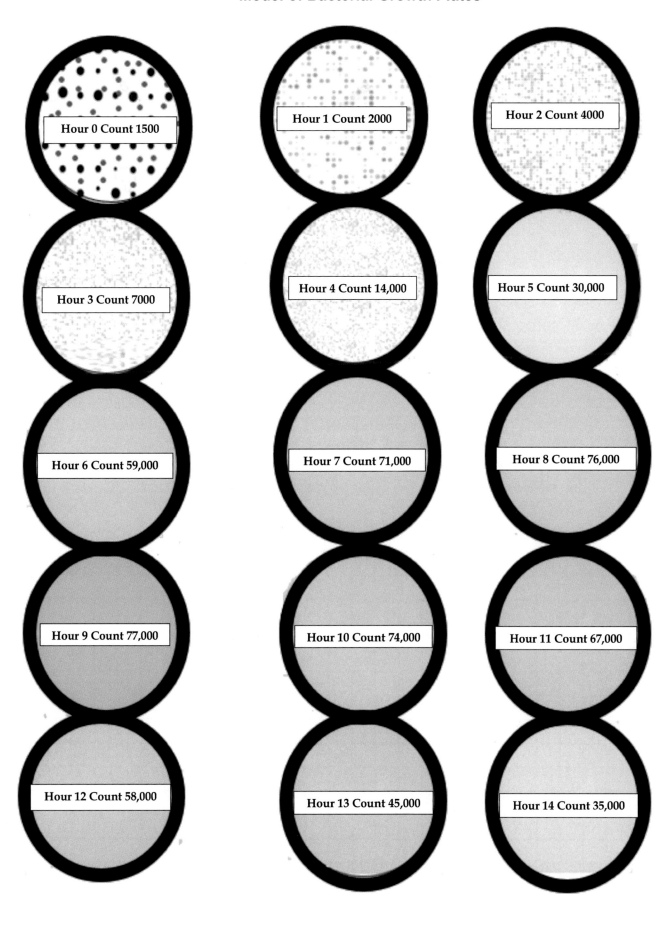

Hour 0 Count 1500

Hour 1 Count 2000

Hour 2 Count 4000

Hour 3 Count 7000

Hour 4 Count 14,000

Hour 5 Count 30,000

Hour 6 Count 59,000

Hour 7 Count 71,000

Hour 8 Count 76,000

Hour 9 Count 77,000

Hour 10 Count 74,000

Hour 11 Count 67,000

Hour 12 Count 58,000

Hour 13 Count 45,000

Hour 14 Count 35,000

Table 1

Growth of Bacterial Population	
Time (hr)	Number of Organisms
0	
1	
2	
3	
4	
5	
6	
7	
8	
9	
10	
11	
12	
13	
14	

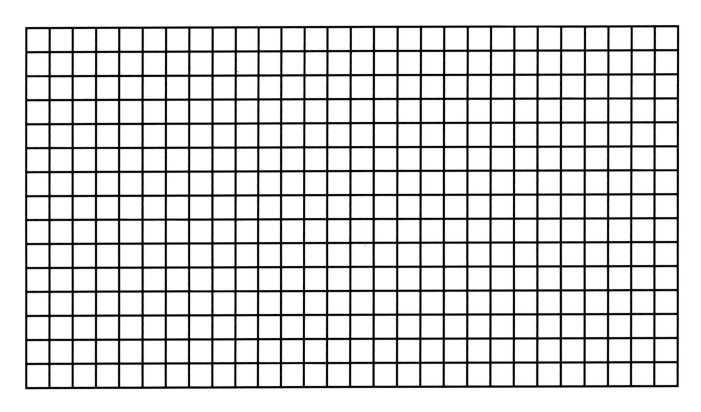

Human Population

The human population is more complex and grows more slowly than the bacterial population just studied. Examine the "Growth in World Population " table 2 which contains the data for the world population up to the year 2000.

Table 2

Growth of World Population	
Year	Estimated Population (in billions)
1200	.3
1300	.3
1400	.4
1500	.4
1600	.5
1700	.6
1800	.8
1830	1.0
1900	1.6
1930	2.0
1960	3.0
1975	4.0
1978	4.2
1981	4.5
2000	6.0

- On the graph paper provided, graph the data from the "Growth in World Population " table. Put TIME IN YEARS on the x-axis (horizontal) and POPULATION on the y-axis (vertical). Title your graph HUMAN POPULATION GROWTH CURVE.
- Plot the data as follows:

- When the graph is completely plotted, label the phases.

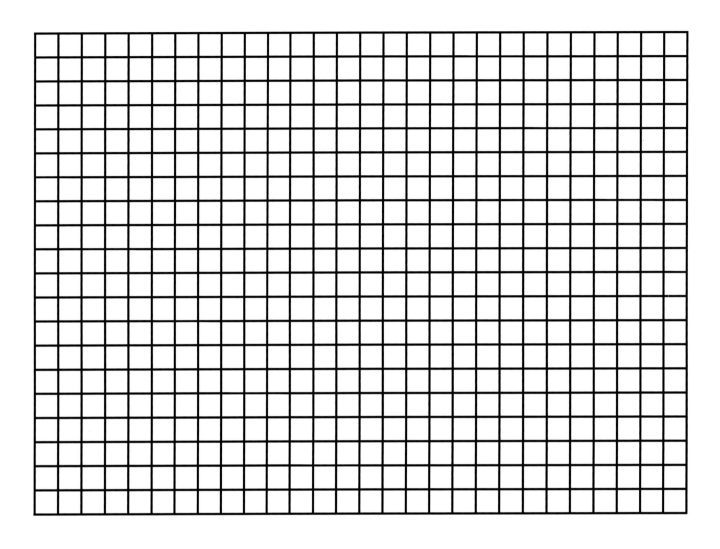

6-How long did it take the human population to double from .5 billion to 1 billion people?

_____

7-How long did it take to double from 2 billion to 4 billion?

_____

8-In which phase of growth is the human population growth curve currently in?

_____

Evolution

Antibiotic Resistance

Liquid hand sanitizer is often used to decrease infectious agents on the hands. Hand washing with soap and water is advisable if contamination can be seen or following the use of the toilet. Many soaps and hand sanitizers are antibacterial. Some labels claim to kill 99.99% of germs (bacteria).

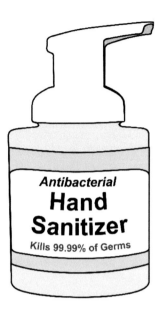

Although 99.99% is *almost* all microbes, what about the 0.01% that are not killed? What do you think would happen to a population of 0.01% of bacteria that are not killed by hand sanitizer? How does this relate to evolution?

1-What do you predict will happen to a population of 0.01% if bacteria not killed by antibacterial hand sanitizer or soap?

_____

_____

_____

_____

In this lab, you will learn about the concept of natural selection as it applies to a current-day issue: Antibacterial Resistance.

Background:

A population is a group of the same kinds of organisms living in the same area. In any population, there is variation in traits among the organisms due to mutation or the recombining of genes from egg and sperm cells. Even bacteria, which reproduce by asexual reproduction (splitting in half), can have offspring that are not exactly the same due to mutations of the DNA or through exchanging DNA with another bacterium. A mutation is a permanent change in the DNA sequence of a gene.

Some traits help an organism survive and some do not help survival. Some traits, like eye coloration, may have no effect on survival. The environment determines which traits are favorable. We say that the environment is the "agent" of natural selection.

Selective pressure is something that changes the ability of an organism to survive in a particular environment. A selective pressure can be something that is living (biotic) or something that is not living (abiotic). Examples of a biotic selective pressures could include predators, prey, or mates. Examples of abiotic selective pressures could include water, weather, or chemicals.

Organisms with favorable traits survive. We call the favorable trait an adaptive advantage because it helps the organism survive. Organisms with an adaptive advantage (favorable traits) pass the genes for those traits on to their offspring. By this mechanism, over time, more and more organisms in a population have the favorable traits. We say the population has evolved and that the organisms have adapted to the environment.

Modeling Natural Selection:

Materials (per group)-1 cup containing 20 Styrofoam nubs, 1 cup containing 8 pebbles, 1 toothpick, 1-8" diameter paper plate, timer

A-Put eight Styrofoam nubs and two pebbles on the same plate in the middle of your group. The nubs and pebbles represent bacteria. Most of the bacteria (nubs) are the same (clones) due to asexual reproduction. They are cylindrical and have a soft "shell". Two of the bacteria (the pebbles) are not like the other clones. They represent bacteria that had mutations resulting in different traits (irregular shape and hard shell).

Note that Table 1 lists 8 "normal" bacteria (nubs) and 2 "mutated" bacteria (pebbles) to start.

The toothpick represents antimicrobial hand sanitizer. You will use the toothpick to catch the bacteria (nubs and pebbles). When you do this, you will be modeling bacteria being destroyed by chemicals in the hand sanitizer. As you complete the modeling activity, you will complete Table 1.

B-Dose #1 (D1) of hand sanitizer. Use the toothpick to pick up—one at a time—and set aside as many of the bacteria as possible in 7 seconds. After 7 seconds, count how many bacteria of each kind are left on the plate. Complete the D1 row in Table 1.

C-Reproduction #1 (R1). Bacteria reproduce by fission. They make clones of themselves. Double the number of any of the remaining bacteria on the plate. For example, if there are three nubs left, make six by adding three more nubs to the plate. If there are two pebbles left, make four by adding two more pebbles to the plate. Complete the R1 row in Table 1.

D-Dose #2 (D2) of hand sanitizer. Use a toothpick to pick up—one at a time—and set aside as many bacteria as possible in 7 seconds. After 7 seconds, count how many bacteria of each kind are left on the plate. Complete the D2 row in Table 1.

E-Reproduction #2 (R2). Double the number of any of the remaining bacteria on the plate. Complete the R2 row in Table 1.

F-Repeat steps D and E above for D3 and R3. Complete the D3 and R3 rows in Table 1.

Table 1: The Effect of Hand Sanitizer on the Number of Normal and Mutated Bacteria

Trials	Number of Normal Bacteria Styrofoam nubs	Number of Mutated Bacteria Pebbles
Start	8	2
Dose 1		
Reproduction 1		
Dose 2		
Reproduction 2		
Dose 3		
Reproduction 3		

Graph 1: Make a double-line graph of your data showing the change in the number of each kind of bacteria over time. Give the graph an appropriate title, and X and Y scales. Create a key using "O" to represent nubs and "X" to represent pebbles.

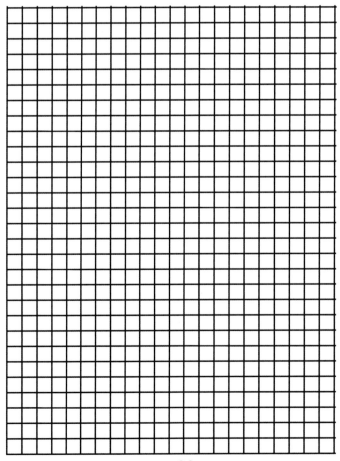

Follow-up Questions:

2-In our model, we started with 8 normal bacteria and 2 mutated bacteria. The normal bacteria were more likely to be "killed"/picked by the hand sanitizer/toothpick. If hand sanitizer were actually effective in killing 8 out of 10 bacteria, what percentage should be on the label? _____

3-The claimed percentage of bacteria killed by many hand sanitizers is 99.99%. How many Styrofoam nubs (normal bacteria) would we need to start with if we were to model 90% effectiveness at killing bacteria? _____

4-Our model was a greatly simplified simulation. If we were to use more accurate numbers to replicate 99.99% effectiveness, we would need many more Styrofoam nubs and pebbles. Since 99.99% = 99.99 out of 100 and it is not possible to have a fractional bacterium (.01 or 1/100), you would need to have 10,000 Styrofoam nubs and 1 pebble in order to create a more accurate model.

If we started with 10,000 Styrofoam nubs and 1 pebble, how long would it take for the population of resistant bacteria to become greater than the population of normal bacteria population?

_____

_____

_____

_____

5-When we used a toothpick to pick up and remove bacteria, that step represented the hand sanitizer killing the bacteria. Which kind of bacteria were killed most easily with every dose of hand sanitizer?

_____

6-What was the selective pressure that determined which bacterial trait was favorable?

_____

Table 2: Bacteria Traits and Their Relative Survival Advantages-(Complete Table)

Traits	Normal Bacteria- Description: cylindrical, soft-bodied, beige	Mutated Bacteria- Description: irregular shape, hard-bodied, tan, brown, black, grey, white
Adaptive Advantage (Traits That Helped Survival)		
Unfavorable Traits		
Unaffected Traits		

7-Choose one trait from Table 2 that was an adaptive advantage. Explain how the trait was an adaptive advantage.

_____

_____

_____

8-Choose one unfavorable trait from Table 2. Explain how the trait was unfavorable.

_____

_____

_____

9-Describe what happens to the bacteria that are not killed by hand sanitizer and explain how this relates to evolution.

_____

_____

_____

_____

_____

10-When a doctor prescribes an antibiotic, the doctor instructs you to take all of the medication until it is gone. This advice should be taken very seriously. If you stop taking the antibiotics too early, what happens to the bacteria that, by chance, have a trait that prevents them from being killed very quickly by the antibiotic?

_____

_____

_____

_____

_____

11-In the same way that hand sanitizer creates resistant bacteria, overuse of antibiotics creates resistant strains of bacteria, as well. Doctors are becoming more and more hesitant to prescribe antibiotics to people if they are sick, especially if the doctor does not know if the sickness is caused by a virus or a bacterium. Why is it a good idea for doctors to be cautious about prescribing antibiotics?

_____

_____

_____

_____

_____

12-Using ideas from this lab, explain why evolution is relevant to our daily lives.

_____

_____

_____

_____

_____

Describing the Elements of Evolution

In each of the following situations describe how evolution by natural selection might have occurred. Use the following terms in your descriptions:

- Overproduction

- Variation

- Survival of the Fittest

- Natural Selection

- Adaptation to the Environment

1- In most terrestrial vertebrates, skull bones are rather rigidly attached to one another, but in snakes they are loosely joined. Most snakes can swallow prey much larger than their heads because their lower jawbones (mandibles) can be rotated downward so that they drop away from the skull; thus the mouth opening is greatly increased. Describe how snakes' mouths might have evolved to have this adaptation according to Darwin's Theory.

_____

_____

_____

_____

_____

_____

2- There are 18,000 to 25,000 species of orchids. Many have extraordinary modifications of flower structure and mechanisms of pollination. In pseudocopulatory pollination, for example, part of the flower is modified to look somewhat like a female insect, and the flower emits a scent that mimics the attractive sex pheromone (scent) of a female bee, fly, or wasp, depending on the orchid species. As a male insect "mates" with the flower, pollen is deposited precisely on that part of the insect's body that will contact the stigma of the next flower visited. Describe how this pseudocopulatory part of the flower may have evolved according to Darwin's Theory.

_____

_____

_____

_____

_____

3- Some bacteria have developed resistance to antibiotics that were once commonly used to treat them. For example, *Staphylococcus aureus* ('golden staph') and *Neisseria gonorrhoeae* (the cause of gonorrhea) are now almost always resistant to benzyl penicillin. In the past, these infections were usually controlled by penicillin. The most serious concern with antibiotic resistance is that some bacteria have become resistant to almost all of the easily available antibiotics. These bacteria are able to cause serious disease and this is a major public health problem. Important examples are methicillin-resistant *Staphylococcus aureus* (MRSA), which can infect the skin, blood, or internal organs and multi-drug-resistant *Mycobacterium tuberculosis* (MDR-TB), which typically infects the lungs. According to Darwin's Theory, how could bacteria have developed a resistance to antibiotics?

_____

_____

_____

_____

_____

4- Deer mice are widespread over North America. They usually have a dark coat so that they blend in with dark soil, which hides them from owls. Over a period of several thousand years they have become more widespread over Nebraska, which has much sandier soil than other areas they inhabit. A pale coat color has evolved in deer mice living in Nebraska. According to Darwin's Theory, how could this have happened?

_____

_____

_____

_____

_____

_____

5- Diamondback moths are insecticide resistant. According to Darwin's Theory, how did they get that way?

_____

_____

_____

_____

_____

_____

6- A plant known as caltrop is found on the Galapagos Islands. On one island it produces fewer seeds and the seeds have tough, spiny coats. That island is also inhabited by many of the bird species *Geospiza fortis*, which eats the contents of the seeds. On another island, where few *Geospiza fortis* exist, the plants produce more seeds and the seed coats have fewer, shorter spines. Use Darwin's Theory to explain this.

_____

_____

_____

_____

_____

7- In a swamp habitat a population of lizards includes the following phenotypes: red, black, brown, and green. Explain which phenotype would confer a selective advantage and why, in 500 years' time, we would likely see the phenotype you chose dominate the population. Use Darwin's Theory to explain your reasoning.

_____

_____

_____

_____

_____

_____

Patterns of Natural Selection

Vocabulary Review: Define the following terms

1-Stabilizing Selection

_____

_____

2-Directional Selection

_____

_____

3-Disruptive Selection

_____

_____

Multiple Choice: Circle the correct answer for each of the questions below.

4-Starlings produce an average of five eggs in each clutch. If there are more than five, the parents cannot adequately feed the young. If there are fewer than five, predators may destroy the entire clutch. This is an example of

    a. disruptive selection.   b. stabilizing selection.

    c. directional selection.   d. none of the above.

5-The occurrence of large or small beak sizes among seed crackers in the absence of medium sized beaks is an example of

    a. directional selection.   b. stabilizing selection.

    c. disruptive selection.   d. none of the above.

6-A scientist measures the circumference of acorns in a population of oak trees and discovers that the most common circumference is 2 cm. What would you expect the most common circumference(s) to be after 10 generations of stabilizing selection?

    a. 2 cm

    b. greater than 2 cm or less than 2 cm

    c. greater than 2 cm and less than 2 cm

    d. can't tell from the information given

7-Refer to question 6, but this time answer what you would expect after 10 generations of disruptive selection.

    a. 2 cm
    b. greater than 2 cm or less than 2 cm
    c. greater than 2 cm and less than 2 cm
    d. can't tell from the information given

8-Refer to question 6, but this time answer what you would expect after 10 generations of directional selection.

    a. 2 cm
    b. greater than 2 cm or less than 2 cm
    c. greater than 2 cm and less than 2 cm
    d. can't tell from the information given

Short Answer: Answer the following questions in complete sentences.

9-What types of individuals in a population are represented by the two ends of a bell curve?

_____

_____

_____

10-At one time, a cow preferred eating white and red four o'clock flowers. Draw a population curve in pencil showing the likely distribution of white, pink and red flowers. Over time, the red flowers started growing spines, discouraging the cow from eating them. Sketch a 2nd distribution curve in pen demonstrating the change. What kind of selection is being demonstrated?

_____

11-Label the three types of selection illustrated by the graphs below.

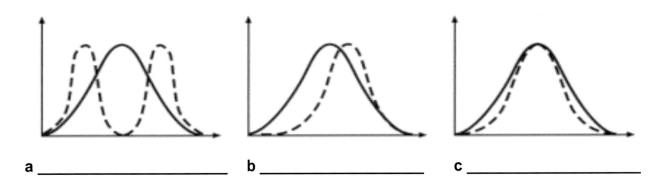

a _____   b _____   c _____

Interpreting Data: Use the following information to answer the questions below.

A population of birds, with various size beaks, eats seeds. Small seeds can be eaten by birds with small beaks. Larger, thicker seeds can only be eaten by birds with larger, thicker beaks. Suppose there is a shortage of small seeds but that there are still many large seeds.

12-Draw a new curve on the graph below to show how the distribution of beak sizes might change as a result of selection in this new environment.

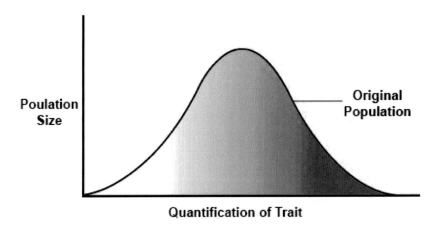

Use the graph above to answer the following questions:

13-Which birds in this population have the highest fitness?

_____

14-Explain how natural selection could lead to the change you predicted.

_____

_____

_____

Graphing:

Scientists have been studying a population of cacti. The population had been in genetic equilibrium, but that changed when a road was built close to the study site. The road keeps away parasitic insects but brings in tourists.

Like other roadside desert areas, passing cactus lovers pick up a souvenir cactus to take home with them after a trip to the desert. The tourists usually take the cacti with a "medium" number of spines.

Years of collecting have taken their toll on the roadside cacti population. A data table of the original and current population is found below:

Original Population (Before Road)		Current Population (After Road)	
Number of Cactus	**Number of Spines**	**Number of Cactus**	**Number of Spines**
4	71	10	72
12	82	22	80
25	95	5	93
13	106	12	108
8	113	14	110
4	122	9	120
2	130	4	129

Using the information above, create a double line graph on the next page. Be sure to:

- Title the graph
- Label the X and Y axis
- Create a key for the differing data lines, using a ○ to indicate the Original Population and a △ to indicate the Current Population
- Graph both the original and current population of cacti

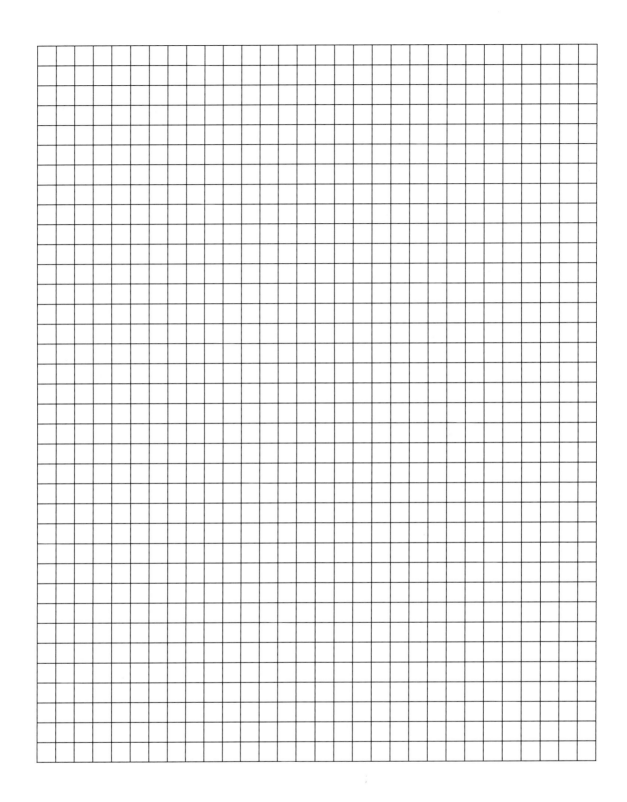

15- This graph shows _____ Selection

Where Do Pandas Fit in the Tree of Life?

Categorizing animals is an inexact science. Certain animals don't perfectly fit into our existing groupings. Pandas are examples of animals that defy classification.

In 1869, a naturalist observed a giant panda and used the descriptor *ursus*, because of its resemblance to bears. Shortly thereafter, another scientist inspected the remains of a giant panda and concluded it was closer to a cat-like creature in the raccoon family called the red panda. This tug-of-war over whether the giant panda is a small bear or big raccoon has been going on for more than a century. In this lab you will learn about some pieces of evidence that scientists have collected relative to the traits of pandas.

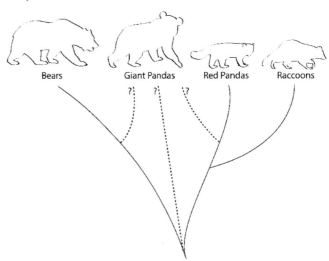

1-Describe the early disagreement about the classification of the giant panda.

_____

_____

Giant Panda

Red Panda

(Drawings not to scale).

Anatomy

Skull- Giant and red pandas have thick skulls with large attachments for jaw muscles, which help them in chewing bamboo stalks.

Raccoon

Red Panda

Black Bear

Giant Panda

2-Compare the tops of the skulls and the upward curve of the lower jaw in the four skulls above.

_____

_____

Front Paws- Giant and red pandas have an opposable "thumb" (highlighted). In both cases, the thumb is actually an enlarged, modified wrist bone. It helps them handle bamboo as they eat it.

| Raccoon | Red Panda | Black Bear | Giant Panda |

3-Compare the "pseudo-thumbs" (fake thumbs) in the four paws above.

_____

_____

4-In terms of the skull and paws, do you think giant pandas and red pandas are closely related? _____Why or why not?

_____

_____

In 1964, biologist D. Dwight Davis published a study of the giant panda and some of its relatives. Davis and his team made observations of the bones, muscles, joints, blood vessels, nerves, brains, glands, organs, of deceased zoo animals. Some of the findings are summarized below.

- The giant panda stands and moves similarly to bears, though it moves less efficiently.

American Black Bear

Giant Panda

100

- The giant panda has similar body proportions to bears. Both can grow to over 200 pounds. Red pandas average 7 to 14 pounds; raccoons average 8 to 20 pounds.

Raccoons   Red Pandas

Bears   Giant Pandas

- Giant pandas and bears have many similarities. Giant pandas differ due to adaptations for diet: larger jaw muscles, opposable "thumbs," and digestive organs.
- Giant pandas and bears both have an extra lobe in their left lungs. Red pandas and raccoons lack the extra lobe.
- Giant pandas and black bears have similar brain structures.

5-In terms of movement, and both internal and external appearance, do you think that giant and red pandas are closely related?_____ Why or why not?

_____

_____

Behavior

Vegetarian Carnivores-Both the giant panda and the red panda live in high-altitude bamboo forests in China. The giant panda eats only bamboo. The red panda eats mostly bamboo, though it sometimes eats other plants, fruit, and insects. The bamboo diet of the two pandas is different from most bears and members of the raccoon family—which tend to eat a variety of plants, fruits, and small animals.

Both giant and red pandas belong to the carnivore lineage, which includes dogs, cats, seals, badgers, and many other animals. To help them cope with their bamboo diet, both pandas have extra-large molars, overgrown jaw muscles, and extra-strong skulls to withstand the force of chewing on tough plant matter. Those characteristics are unusual for carnivores.

6-What is the only thing that giant pandas eat?   _____

7-Describe the diet of red pandas. _____

8-Unlike other carnivores (meat eating animals), what characteristics do giant and red pandas share?

_____

101

Fossils

Fossils can provide clues as to what the panda's ancestors may have looked like. *Ailuropoda baconi* looked almost identical to the modern giant panda, though it was much larger. Its fossilized remains have been found in a much larger range than pandas currently live in today. *Ailuropoda microta* was half the size of a modern giant panda. It looked much like modern giant pandas, but its skull was less specialized for eating bamboo, though it did eat tough plants. It was slightly more bear-like. *Ailurarctos*, the "Lefung panda," was even more bear-like, showing only precursors of the giant panda's specializations for eating bamboo. *Kretzoiarctos Beatrix* is a bear that lived about 12 million years ago, the shape and wear patterns on the teeth suggest that, like the giant panda, its diet included tough plants. As of February 2018, scientists have not found any fossils with traits that are intermediate between the giant and red pandas.

9-The fossil evidence suggests that the giant pandas' ancient ancestors where b_____-like but ate t_____ p_____.

Both the giant panda and the red panda have an enlarged wrist bone that serves as an opposable "thumb" that helps the paws hold and manipulate bamboo. Over the years, some scientists have argued that this enlarged wrist bone must have been present in a bamboo-eating ancestor to both pandas, and others have argued that it could have arisen later and separately in both pandas

10-Besides similarities in jaws and teeth, the giant panda and red panda both have enlarged w_____ (radial sesamoid) bones that they use as a "pseudo" (fake) t_____.

Simocyon batalleri lived between about 5 and 12 million years ago. Among fossilized remains that were found are forelimbs, which had an enlarged wrist bone (the radial sesamoid).

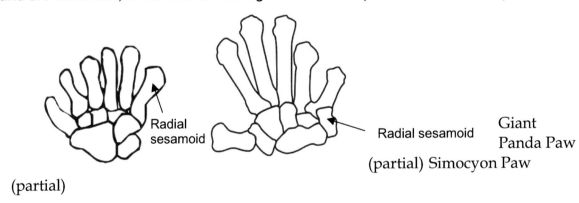

Radial sesamoid

(partial)

Radial sesamoid

Giant Panda Paw

(partial) Simocyon Paw

Simocyon shared many traits with modern red pandas, and the two clearly belong to the same lineage. However, *Simocyon* did not have the large, flattened molars or extra-strong jaw muscles of the red panda. Instead, its teeth look more like those of carnivores, suggesting that this ancestor did not eat bamboo or any other tough plants.

Researchers hypothesize that the "thumb" was not used for handling bamboo, but rather to help the animal hold onto thin tree branches as it walked along them.

In a 2015 study, researchers measured the radial sesamoid bones in several carnivores, both fossilized and living. They learned that this bone is enlarged in many carnivores, especially those that spend time in trees. The table below shows the size of the radial sesamoid bone relative to the size of the animals' paws.

Species	Relative Size of Radial Sesamoid	Time Spent in Trees
Giant Panda	0.84	▭
Wolverine	0.51	◼▢
Simocyon Batalleri	0.51	◼▢
Fisher	0.50	◼
Pine Marten	0.46	◼▢
Red Panda	0.45	◼
Asian Bearcat	0.44	◼
Indarctos Arctoides (ancestral bear)	0.40	▭

11-According to the table above, why might giant and red pandas *not* be that closely related?

_____

Biochemistry

DNA Hybridization- Single-stranded DNA molecules will "hybridize" with each other through complementary base pairing as long as their DNA sequences are similar enough. The chart below shows the ability of different species' DNA to hybridize with one another. A lower number of "stability units" means that the DNA sequences were more similar, and the DNA hybridized at a higher rate.

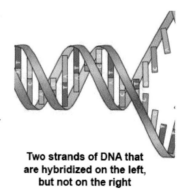

Two strands of DNA that are hybridized on the left, but not on the right

103

	Brown Bear	Giant Panda	Red Panda	Raccoon
Brown Bear	-	4.3	14.0	14.4
Giant Panda	4.8	-	14.4	14.2
Red Panda	13.9	14.1	-	14.3
Raccoon	14.4	14.7	13.9	-
Dog (Control)	18.7	18.3	18.9	18.5

12-Which animals had the most similar DNA according to the chart above?

Chromosome Number- Different species have different numbers of chromosomes. Chromosomes are normally loosely spread out, but when a cell is getting ready to divide, its chromosomes condense so that, with the aid of a microscope, individual chromosomes are visible. The table below shows the number of chromosomes in several species.

Organism	Number of Chromosomes
Raccoon	19 pairs
Red Panda	22 pairs
Giant Panda	21 pairs
American Black Bear	37 pairs
Sun Bear	37 pairs
Polar Bear	37 pairs
Spectacled Bear	26 pairs

13-Which animal(s) did the giant panda's chromosome number most closely match?

Chromosome Shape and Banding Patterns-

When chromosomes are dyed to make them more visible, a pattern of bands appears. Banding patterns are the same for all members of a species and similar between related species. Giant panda chromosomes are relatively large, and most of them have a centromere (the skinny, pinched-in area) near the center. Most bear chromosomes, in contrast, are on the smaller side with a centromere close to one end.

Chromosome Banding Patterns

1 2 3 4 5
Giant panda chromosomes

1 2 3 4 5
Brown bear chromosomes

14-Compare the shape of the giant panda's chromosomes to the shape of the brown bear's chromosomes.

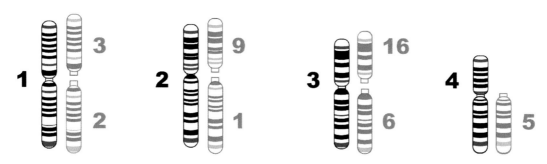

Giant panda (left in each pair) and black bear (right in each pair) chromosomes lined up together

When scientists compared the banding patterns of bear and giant panda chromosomes, they observed that the chromosomes lined up together. Giant panda chromosomes do not line up this way with chromosomes from the red panda or members of the raccoon family.

15-Although the position of the centromere differed on giant panda and black bear chromosomes, their chromosomal b_____ p_____ matched.

Hemoglobin Sequences- Hemoglobin is a protein that is found in red blood cells. It picks up oxygen from the lungs or gills and delivers it to all the tissues in the body. Nearly every vertebrate animal makes hemoglobin proteins. Though the proteins do the same job, there are slight variations in their amino acid sequences and in the DNA sequences of the genes that code for them. The following table shows the pair-wise comparisons of the beta amino acid sequences of hemoglobin proteins (a subunit of hemoglobin). The giant panda and red panda had few differences.

Species	Number of Amino Acid Differences (287 total)
Giant Panda vs. Red Panda	6
Giant Panda vs. Polar Bear	11
Red Panda vs. Raccoon	18

16-According to the chart above, the giant panda and red panda have the fewest differences in h_____ amino acid sequences.

To summarize, both giant and red pandas eat bamboo, grip bamboo the same way and share similar snout, teeth and paw features, as well as a resemblance. The giant panda is bear like because it has a very similar shape, size, walk, and ability to climb.

It might be possible that the giant panda and red panda developed similar features due to convergent evolution, a process where organisms not closely related independently evolve similar traits as a result of having to adapt to similar environments or ecological niches. It is also possible that convergent evolution explains the panda's resemblance to bears.

Some scientists argue that we need to revisit the classification of the red panda to see if it is accurately grouped with raccoons. Since the development of DNA technology, scientists have pursued these avenues to answer these questions. Some DNA studies have shown that the giant panda is closer to the bear family while the red panda is indeed closer to the raccoon family. Nevertheless, these results are inconclusive, and the argument remains unresolved.

Renowned biologist George B. Schaller prefers that the giant panda retain its mystery and individuality, saying, "the panda is a panda". He quips that, as the panda lives quietly in the mountains of Szechuan, it "pseudothumbs his nose at us".

17-What Do You Think? Review the previous pages as you complete the chart.

Which Lineage Are Giant Pandas Most Similar To? B = Bears / R = Red Pandas & Racoons / Mixed	
Evidence:	**B or R or M?**
Anatomy-Skull	
Anatomy-Teeth	
Anatomy-Front Paw/Pseudothumb	
Anatomy-Body Size	
Anatomy-Skeleton	
Anatomy-Muscles	
Anatomy-Internal Organs	
Behavior-Diet	
Fossils	
Biochemistry-DNA Hybridization	
Biochemistry-Number of Chromosomes	
Biochemistry-Chromosome shape and Banding Patterns	
Biochemistry-Hemoglobin Amino Acid Sequences	

18-In your final analysis, which lineage do you believe giant pandas are closest to and why?

_____

_____

Genetics

Animal Body Plans: Homeobox Genes

A body plan is essentially the blueprint for the way the body of an organism is laid out. An organism's symmetry, its number of body segments, and number of limbs are all aspects of its body plan. The body plan is a key feature of an organism's morphology (structure). Since the discovery of DNA, developmental biologists have been able to learn a lot about how genes control the development of structural features through a series of processes that act as position indicators for cells. A key finding was the existence of groups of homeobox genes, which are responsible for laying down the basic body plan in organisms.

Homeobox genes are conserved (similar) between species as diverse as the fruit fly and man. Indeed, the basic segmented pattern of the worm or fruit fly is the precursor of the segmented spine in man. Homeobox genes are why all vertebrates, from salamanders to humans, look very similar in the early stages of their embryonic development. There a several other similarities and trends among the animal kingdom, as well.

1-What are some aspects of an organism's morphology?

_____

_____

_____

2-What do homeobox genes do?

_____

_____

Within the animal kingdom several evolutionary trends and advancements are seen. Most animals have a body plan best described as a tube within a tube. This plan calls for two openings: one for food to enter the body (mouth) and one for wastes to leave the body (anus). The "tube-within-a-tube" plan allows specialization of parts along the tube, such as a stomach, intestine, etc.

A sac-like body plan has only one opening for both food intake and waste removal. Sac-like body plan animals do not have tissue specialization or development of organs. Animals with the "tube-within-a-tube" plan are more efficient at digesting and absorbing their food than animals with the sac-like body plan.

3-What is the benefit of a "tube-within-a-tube" body instead of a sac-like body?

_____

_____

Many, but not all, animals produce three embryonic tissue layers as they develop: the endoderm (develops into digestion and respiration structures), mesoderm (develops into muscles, bones, blood, skin, and reproductive organs), and ectoderm (develops into skin, brain, and nervous system). Some animals, most notably sponges, lack these tissue layers. Cnidarians (a group including coral and jellyfish) have only two of these layers and are termed diploblastic. Flatworms, ribbon worms, humans, etc. have all three tissue layers, and are triploblastic.

4-Humans are triploblastic. List our tissue layers in the following order: outside, middle, inside.

_____

_____

Asymmetrical animals (e.g. sponges) have no general body plan or axis of symmetry that divides the body into mirror-image halves. Within the animal kingdom this appears to be a primitive condition. More advanced animals have symmetry. Radially symmetrical animals (such as coral and jelly fish) have body parts organized about a central axis with multiple planes of symmetry. Radially symmetrical animals are often, for some part of their life, nonmotile (not capable of movement), and live attached to a substrate (surface). Radial symmetry allows animals, such as jellyfish, corals, and sea anemones, to reach out in all directions from one central point. Bilaterally symmetrical animals (such as humans) have only a single plane of symmetry that produces mirror halves. Bilaterally symmetrical animals tend to be active and to move forward at an anterior end, which eventually led to concentration of sensory organs in the anterior end, or head.

5-Identify what kind of animal each of these are (asymmetrical, radially symmetrical, or bilaterally symmetrical). Draw a line of symmetry through the animal's body wherever possible.

_____   _____

Some animals have their bodies divided into segments. Segmentation allows them to specialize certain segments, such as for antennae, eyes, claws, legs, etc. Humans, insects, and earthworms are examples of segmented animals. The genes controlling segmentation in different organisms are the same.

6-Of what value is body segmentation?

_____

_____

_____

_____

Certain genes called homeotic genes (homeo = alike) are similar in structure and function in all animals; they serve as molecular architects and direct the building of bodies according to definite plans.

Like many other breakthroughs in genetics, this one came from the fruit fly (drosophila). Fruit flies are highly specialized insects with 2 wings and 3 body segments. The fruit fly embryo starts out with a series of 16 equal-sized segments. Various segments merge to make the 3 segments we recognize as the head, thorax, and abdomen.

In the 1940s, it was found that mutations in a cluster of genes, called the bithorax complex, caused duplication of a body segment with an extra pair of wings in drosophila. These genes were acting as master switches, turning on and off groups of other genes involved in body shape, and controlling the number, pattern, position, and fusion of segments and appendages.

7-In drosophila, what does the cluster of genes that affect body segmentation do?

_____

_____

In the late 1970s, the homeotic genes controlling the development of the drosophila's body were sequenced. It was observed that in each of these genes a particular DNA segment 180 bases long was virtually identical. This DNA sequence, called the homeobox, translates into a protein sequence 60 amino acids in length. This protein sequence binds to DNA and switches on and off the process of transcription, the expression of genes into proteins. By controlling the transcription in all cells, homeobox (hox) genes act as master switches determining cell fates, growth, and development.

8-What do hox genes control?

_____

_____

_____

_____

Hox genes in mice and humans are very similar in number and chromosomal arrangement. It is remarkable that only about 40 genes out of a total of about 100,000 control most of the development, architecture, and appearance of the body plan of complex mammalian species.

As different as the adult fly and mouse appear, their homeotic genes had a common evolutionary origin, shown by the marked similarity in homeobox sequences. The fly and mouse had a common ancestor half a billion years ago, but the homeobox sequence has hardly changed during that long time period.

9-About how many hox genes control the appearance of the body plans in mammals? _____

10-Why do scientists think that the fly and mouse have a common evolutionary origin?

_____

_____

The same hox genes that determine the belly side of invertebrates establish the back side of vertebrates. Similarly, hox genes provide spectacular insight into the evolution of the eye. The eyes of octopuses, flies, and humans appear very different, yet in 1994 it was discovered that the hox gene responsible for induction of the drosophila eye is virtually identical to the one that induces the mouse eye. This hox gene switches on eye formation in creatures that see. All eyes of all organisms have a common evolutionary origin.

11-What do bellies of invertebrates have to do with the backs of vertebrates?

_____

_____

12-The eyes of different animals appear dissimilar, yet they are related. How do we know?

_____

_____

DNA Fingerprinting/Profiling

This activity is a simulation of how evidence can be analyzed in a murder case. Your role is that of a laboratory technician.

Three suspects have been identified with possible links to a murder victim. You will use a technique called DNA fingerprinting/DNA profiling to compare DNA collected from each of the three suspects to minute (tiny) amounts of DNA left at the crime scene in the form of blood, semen, hair, saliva, or skin cells.

Blood and skin cells were also found under the fingernails of the victim. DNA from this evidence has previously been analyzed by other technicians in your lab. The results will be provided to you. You will be analyzing DNA samples from the victim and three suspects to see if any match the DNA from beneath the victim's fingernails.

1-What possible reason(s) could there be for skin and/or blood cells to be under a victim's fingernails?

_____

_____

_____

With the exception of identical twins, no two people have the same DNA sequence. DNA profiling can be used to compare the DNA of different individuals so that small differences in each person's genetic makeup can be seen. The technique results in a photograph with a pattern of dark bands that reflect the composition of a DNA molecule. Since these banding patterns are unique to each person, they are called a DNA profile or DNA fingerprint.

2-Why is the term "DNA fingerprinting" an accurate name for the technique?

_____

_____

Once DNA samples are obtained, the process of DNA fingerprinting can begin. DNA fingerprinting involves three steps. The first step is using a restriction enzyme to digest, or cut, the DNA samples into small fragments. A restriction enzyme is an enzyme that recognizes and binds with a specific short base sequence of DNA. The restriction enzyme cuts the DNA samples at specific sites within the sequence. This results in DNA fragments of various lengths.

3-What is a restriction enzyme?

_____

_____

4-What does a restriction enzyme do?

_____

_____

The second step in DNA fingerprinting is to separate the DNA fragments by size. This is done by a technique called gel electrophoresis. The DNA is placed on a jelly-like slab (gel) on a tray. The gel is exposed to an electric current. DNA has a negative electrical charge, so the fragments are attracted to the positive pole when the electric current is applied. Smaller fragments travel farther up the gel than longer ones.

5-What does the gel electrophoresis technique do to DNA fragments?

_____

_____

6-Why are DNA fragments attracted to the positive pole?

_____

7-How does the size of the DNA fragments affect their mobility in the gel?

_____

Step three is to transfer the separated DNA fragments from the gel in a technique that then labels them with a radioactive marker. The radioactive markers then expose film wherever they bind to the DNA fragments. The film is developed, and dark bands mark the lengths of the DNA fragments. This process is called autoradiography. The resulting pattern is unique to each individual.

8-An autoradiograph is a picture showing the b_____ p_____ of the

different lengths of DNA f_____.

PROCEDURE:

A-Obtain simulated DNA samples from the following: The Victim; Suspect #1; Suspect #2; Suspect #3

B-Obtain the simulated restriction enzymes: RI; R2; R3; R4

C-Place the victim's DNA sample in front of you. To see if any of the restriction enzymes (R1, R2, R3, and R4) will cut this sample, note the placement of the arrow in relation to the A's, T's, C's, and G's. Place a "cut line" with your pencil wherever is appropriate, according to the restriction enzymes "rule". **IMPORTANT: Keep the DNA one long strand until all pencil "cut lines" have been placed.**

D-After the DNA has been exposed to all four restriction enzymes use your scissors to cut the DNA sample where each enzyme indicates it should be cut.

E-Separate the cut DNA fragments by size.

F-When gel electrophoresis is run, longer DNA fragments will move toward the top (negative) end of the gel and smaller fragments will move toward the bottom (positive) end of the gel. Count how many codons each of the DNA fragments is and place a dark line at that number on the simulated gel electrophoresis tray in the victim's column. For example, this fragment is 2 codons long:

```
GGC  TTT
CCG  AAA
```

NOTICE that the sample taken from the skin cells from under the victim's fingernails has been done for you.

G-Repeat steps C-F for each of the suspect's DNA samples.

SIMULATED GEL ELECTROPHORESIS TRAY

NEGATIVE (-) POLE

Number of Codons	victim	suspect #1	suspect #2	suspect #3	skin cells from under victim's fingernails
10	( )	( )	( )	( )	( )
9	( )	( )	( )	( )	( )
8	( )	( )	( )	( )	( )
7	( )	( )	( )	( )	( )
6	( )	( )	( )	( )	( )
5	( )	( )	( )	( )	(▬)
4	( )	( )	( )	( )	( )
3	( )	( )	( )	( )	(▬)
2	( )	( )	( )	( )	(▬)
1	( )	( )	( )	( )	(▬)

POSITIVE (+) POLE

Interpretation of the results is done by comparing the banding patterns of the DNA samples. If any of the DNA sample banding patterns are identical, that is a positive match. *(In a "real" situation an autoradiograph would be made from the gel results.)*

114

9-Did the victim scratch him/her self?

_____

10-How do you know?

_____

11-Which, if any, of the suspects matches the skin cells from under the victim's fingernails?

_____

12-If one of the suspect's DNA is found under the (dead) victim's fingernails, what does this

suggest?

_____

_____

13-Imagine that you are on a jury and actual DNA fingerprinting evidence (not simulated, as in this lab) is introduced as evidence. Explain why you would or would not find such evidence believable.

_____

_____

_____

_____

Restriction Enzymes:

Cut on the dotted lines.

R1	**ACT** ⬆ **TAT**
R2	**TTT** **CAT** ⬆
R3	**ACA** ⬆ **GGG**
R4	⬆ **AGG** **CCT**

DNA Samples:

Cut on the dotted lines.

NOTE: "Real" restriction enzymes don't "see" codons as is shown here. Rather, they recognize specific base patterns no matter where on the DNA they occur.

Victim's DNA sample

3' TGA ATA CTA AAA GTA AAG TCT CCT TAC CCC TTC 5'
5' ACT TAT GAT TTT CAT TTC AGA GGA TTG GGG AAG 3'

Suspect #1's DNA sample

3' TTT ACT AAA GTA CGC TTT TTC AGA TGT CCC ACC 5'
5' AAA TGA TTT CAT GCG AAA AAG TCT ACA GGG TGG 3'

Suspect #2's DNA sample

3' AGA TTG TGA ATA CCC TTG CCC TTG AGA TCC GGA 5'
5' TCT AAC ACT TAT GGG AAC GGG AAC TCT AGG CCT 3'

Suspect #3's DNA sample

3' AGA AGA TTG AAA GTA GGA TGA ATA AGA TGT CCC 5'
5' TCT TCT AAC TTT CAT CCT ACT TAT TCT ACA GGG 3'

119

Protein Synthesis

Materials: Various colored squares, tape or glue stick

The information encoded in the nucleotide sequence of DNA is not used directly in the synthesis of proteins (polypeptides). Instead, the information carried on the DNA molecule is transcribed to a molecule of messenger RNA (m-RNA). The site of the synthesis of the protein is the ribosome where the various amino acids needed to synthesize the protein are brought by molecules of transfer RNA (t-RNA).

DNA Replication

The following is the base sequence on one strand of a molecule of DNA that will serve as our template:

CGATTGGCAGTCATAGGCTAAGAT ←

1-Give the base sequence of the complementary DNA strand below.
(To make DNA replication easier, draw lines between each set of three bases in the template strand above).

— —

Transcription

Messenger RNA (m-RNA) is synthesized from the template DNA strand during the process of transcription. This m-RNA code will then travel to the ribosome where its code will be translated into an amino acid sequence to construct the polypeptide chain (protein).

2- The bases on the m-RNA are read three at a time. Each of these nucleotide triplets are known as a codon. Transcribe the template DNA strand above as m-RNA codons.

Amino
Acid
Code [____ _____ _____ _____ _____ _____ _____ _____]

[- — - — - — - — - — - — - — - — -] m-RNA
Code

Amino
Acid
Color [____ _____ _____ _____ _____ _____ _____ _____]

PROTEIN SYNTHESIS/Translation
You will soon construct a model of the protein that would be made from the m-RNA transcribed above. First, use the charts to write the amino acid code and color above and below the m-RNA sequence you just transcribed above.

Genetic Code Chart

	U	C	A	G
UU	phe	phe	phe	phe
UC	ser	ser	ser	ser
UA	tyr	tyr	term	term
UG	up	up	term	trp
CU	leu	leu	leu	leu
CC	pro	pro	pro	pro
CA	his	his	gin	gin
CG	arg	arg	arg	arg
AU	ile	ile	ile	met
AC	thr	thr	thr	thr
AA	asn	asn	lys	lys
AG	ser	ser	arg	arg
GU	val	val	val	vak
GC	ala	ala	ala	ala
GA	asp	asp	glu	glu
GG	gly	gly	gly	gly

Find the 1st 2 letters of the m-RNA codon

Find the 3rd letter of the m-RNA codon

Amino Acid Abbreviation/Color Chart: Using Paper Squares of Various Colors

ABBREVIATION	AMINO ACID	COLOR
gly	glycine	pink
ala	alanine	white
val	valine	black
ile	isoleucine	lt. blue
leu	leucine	drk. Blue
ser	serine	red
thr	threonine	black
pro	proline	brown
asp	aspartate	yellow
glu	glutamine	lt. blue
lys	lysine	pink
arg	arginine	orange
asm	asparagine	green
gln	glutamine	pink
cys	cysteine	drk. Blue
met	methionine	red
trp	tryptophan	brown
phe	phenylalanine	yellow
tyr	tyrosine	white
his	histidine	orange
term	termination	green

122

Sometimes errors occur in the replication of DNA or external agents change the normal sequence of nucleotides. These changes are known as mutations and they change the normal sequence of the amino acids in the polypeptide chain (protein). This results in an abnormal protein being constructed.

If the fourth nucleotide in the template DNA strand from the 1st page of this lab was changed from T to A the following DNA base sequence code would result:

(This is called a substitution gene mutation.)

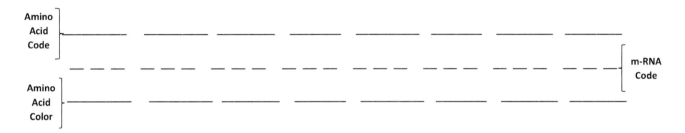

CGAATGGCAGTCATAGGCTAAGAT

3-Transcribe the mutated DNA strand above. (To make transcription easier, draw lines between each set of three bases in the mutated template strand above). Since the bases on m-RNA are read as nucleotide triplets (or codons), that is the way you will write them below:

You will soon construct a model of the protein that would be made from this mutated m-RNA molecule. First, use the genetic code chart and color chart previous page to write the amino acid code and color above and below the transcribed sequence above.

If G were added to the template DNA strand (from the 1st page of this lab) after the third nucleotide, the following DNA base sequence code would result:

(This is called an addition gene mutation.)

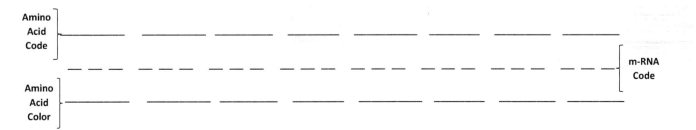

CGAGTTGGCAGTCATAGGCTAAGAT

4-Transcribe the mutated DNA strand above. (To make transcription easier, draw lines between each set of three bases in the mutated template strand above). Since the bases on the m-RNA are read as nucleotide triplets (or codons), that is the way you will write them below:

You will soon construct a model of the protein that would be made from this mutated m-RNA molecule. First, use the genetic code chart and color code chart to write the amino acid code and color above and below the transcribed sequence above.

Now construct the three protein chains using the amino acid codes & colors you wrote on the 1st and 3rd pages of this lab. Obtain the appropriate colored paper squares (which represent amino acids). Tape them in the order indicated in the translated sequences on the 1st page (number 2) and the 3rd page (numbers 3 and 4) of this lab.

Disregard any extra nucleotides that are not part of a codon.

After you have taped your three protein/polypeptide chains down and labeled them, answer the following question:

5-If the first m-RNA strand you transcribed (#2) represented a "normal" protein, explain the results of the other two m-RNA strands (#s 3 & 4) you created in terms of what type of mutations occurred in each and how the resulting proteins that were formed were changed.

_____

_____

_____

_____

_____

_____

_____

_____

_____

Normal Protein #2	Mutated Protein #3	Mutated Protein #4

No Mutation	Type of Mutation: _____	Type of Mutation: _____

Name_____ **Date**_____ **Period**_____ **Lab**_____

Variations Within a Population

Members of a species are not all exactly alike. Small differences, called variations, exist in each member of a species. Variations are found in all organisms. Some variations may be passed on to offspring of organisms through reproduction. Most inherited variations are neutral; that is, they do not affect the survival of the organism. Some variations are helpful. Helpful inherited variations are called adaptations. Harmful inherited variations will cause the organism to be less well-suited to its environment.

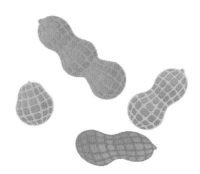

The process by which organisms with adaptations to the environment survive is called natural selection/evolution. Natural selection/evolution tends to allow well-adapted organisms to reproduce and pass the beneficial trait to their offspring. Organisms with harmful traits will die off. This process is sometimes referred to as "survival of the fittest"

In this investigation, you will observe variations that exist in one type of plant as well as within your classroom population.

Problem: How can the variations within plant and animal populations be measured?

Materials

10 peanuts in shells, metric ruler, colored pencils, graph paper

Part A. Variation within a Species of Plants

1-Measure the length of each peanut shell in millimeters. Record the measurements in Data Table 1 below.

Data Table 1: Observations-Measurement of Peanut Shells in Millimeters

Peanut Shell 1	Peanut Shell 2	Peanut Shell 3	Peanut Shell 4	Peanut Shell 5	Peanut Shell 6	Peanut Shell 7	Peanut Shell 8	Peanut Shell 9	Peanut Shell 10

2-Share your results with your class.

3-Copy the class results onto Data Table 2 below.

Data Table 2: Class Peanut Shell Data (Number of Shells of Each Length)

Lengths (mm)										
Total Number of Each Length										

4-Using the data in Data Table 2, construct a bar graph for the peanut shell lengths on the graph paper below.

Lengths of Peanut Shells

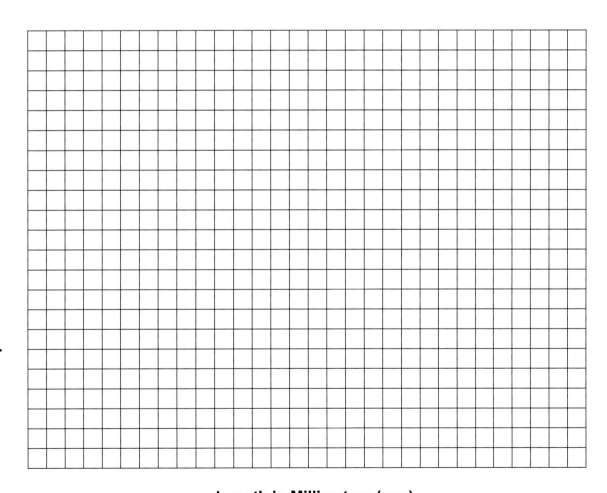

Length in Millimeters (mm)

B. Variation within a species of Animal

5-Measure your handspan (the tip of your thumb to the tip of your pinky in an outstretched hand). Round off the measurement to the nearest centimeter. Record your hand span in Data Table 3 below.

Data Table 3: Length of Individual's Handspan

My Own Handspan (cm)	

6-Share the results with your class.

7-Copy the class results into Data Table 4 below.

Data Table 4: Comparison of Handspans for the Class

Measurements of Handspans in cm																	
Number of Students																	

8-Using the data in Data Table 4, construct a bar graph of hand span results using the graph paper on the next page.

Handspans of Students

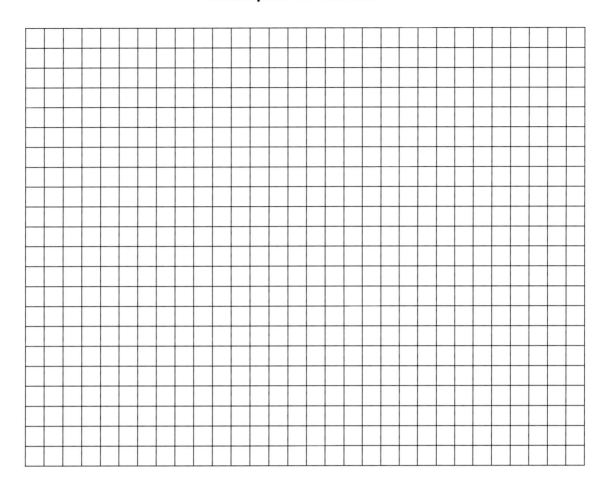

Length in Centimeters (cm)

Population data, like the variations we've been examining in this lab, can be "distributed" (spread out) in different ways. They can distribute:

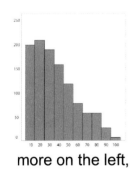

more on the left,

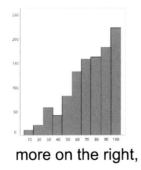

more on the right,

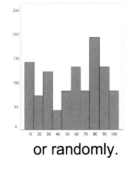

or randomly.

But often, data tends to be around a central value with no bias left or right:

This is called a normal distribution or a "bell curve". Heights of people, marks on a test, birthweight, and shoe size are just a few examples of things that are normally distributed.

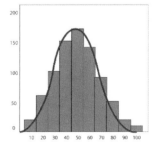

Analysis and Conclusions

A-What is meant by the term variation?

_____

_____

B-What length(s) were most common among peanut shells?

_____

C-What length(s) were least common among peanut shells?

_____

D-What is the general shape of the peanut shell graph?

_____

E-What handspan length(s) were most common in the class?

_____

F-What handspan length(s) were least common in the class?

_____

G-What is the general shape of the handspan graph?

_____

Critical Thinking and Application

H-Peanuts, like beans and peas, are legumes. Legumes are edible seeds which are enclosed in pods. There are variations in legume pod sizes. How might a large pod (shell) size be a beneficial adaptation for plant reproduction?

_____

_____

_____

I-There are variations in human hand spans. How might a large hand span be a beneficial adaptation for human survival?

_____

_____

_____

J-There are variations in the number of seeds per pod in legumes. Why would having more than one seed in a pod be beneficial adaptation to a bean plant?

_____

_____

_____

K-There are variations in plant root systems. Why would having a very short root system be a harmful adaptation to a desert cactus plant?

_____

_____

_____

L-There are variations in animal coat colors. How is the white coat color of certain arctic animals a helpful adaptation in the Winter?

_____

_____

_____

Human Body Systems

Digestive System

Materials: 5 different colors of yarn (purple, yellow, blue, orange, brown), Scissors, Metric Ruler, Calculator

We eat food because it gives us energy we need to work, grow and repair our cells. We get energy from food by digesting it. This doesn't just mean digesting it into smaller chunks, this means breaking it down into its building blocks: proteins into amino acids, complex carbohydrates into sugars, and fats into fatty acids and glycerol.

The digestive system is long and contains multiple organs to help break down food and adsorb nutrients. Our digestive systems use both mechanical and chemical digestion to break food into simple molecules. Mechanical digestion involves physically breaking the food down into smaller pieces without any chemical changes to the food. Chemical digestion involves enzymes breaking the chemical bonds in food into nutrient components.

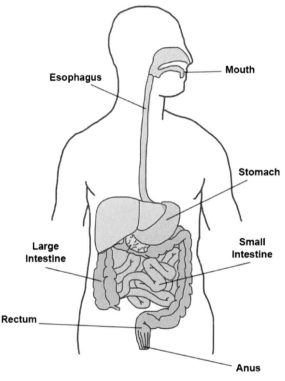

The **mouth** is the first organ in the digestive system. Both chemical digestion and physical digestion occur in the mouth. The **esophagus** connects the mouth to the stomach. No digestion occurs in the esophagus. The **stomach** contains hydrochloric acid and gastric juices which help to chemically digest proteins. Mechanical digestion also occurs in the stomach due to the churning motion. The **small intestine** is the longest part of the digestive system, and most of the nutrients are absorbed there. In the small intestine, other digestive juices from the **pancreas** and **liver** are added. These juices help chemically digest food. The **large intestine** is the site of water reclamation for the body.

The diagram to the right shows that the digestive system is one long tube that contains many parts that are folded up inside the body. If the digestive system were removed from a human body and laid out flat, it would be much longer than it appears in this diagram.

In this lab we will make a model of the length of our own digestive systems by measuring & cutting yarn to represent lengths of different parts of the system. We will tape the pieces of yarn together so we can visualize the entire length of the digestive system.

Procedure-Work with a partner (of similar height, if possible). Take turns being the "model" and "measurer":

- Use **purple yarn** to represent the beginning of digestion in the mouth.
  Model: Stretch the yarn from the front of your lips to the back of your jaw.
  Measurer: Cut and measure the yarn in centimeters (cm).
  Record the length of the "mouth" in the Digestive System Data Table.

- Use **yellow yarn** to represent the esophagus.
  Model: Stretch the yarn from the back of your jaw to just below your xiphoid process (the end of your ribcage, in the center).
  Measurer: Cut and measure the yarn in cm.
  Record the length of the "esophagus" yarn in the Digestive System Data Table.
  Tape the esophagus yarn to the mouth yarn.

- Use **blue yarn** to represent the stomach.
  Model: Stretch the yarn across your handspan, from thumb to pinky.
  Measurer: Cut and measure the yarn in cm.
  Record the length of the "stomach" yarn in the Digestive System Data Table.
  Tape the stomach yarn to the esophagus yarn.

- Use **orange yarn** to represent the small intestine.
  Model: Stand up.
  Measurer: Measure your partner's height in cm (1 m = 100 cm). Multiply the measurement by four. That is the number of cm you will cut the yarn.
  Show your math here:

  Record the length of the "small intestine" yarn in cm in the Digestive System Data Table.
  Tape the small intestine yarn to the stomach yarn.

- Use **brown yarn** to represent the large intestine.
  Model: Stand up.
  Measurer: Measure your partner's height in cm.
  Cut the yarn in this measurement.
  Record the length of the "large intestine" yarn in cm in the Digestive System Data Table.
  Tape the large intestine yarn to the small intestine yarn.
  Add the numbers to get the approximate total length of the digestive tract.

My height in cm: _____   **My height in M:** _____

Digestive System Data Table

DIGESTIVE ORGAN	LENGTH (CM)
Mouth	
Esophagus	
Stomach	
Small Intestine	
Large Intestine	
TOTAL	

<u>Convert</u> this to meters using the formula: (total # of centimeters)

Total # of cm   X   0.01   =   total # of M

Approximate length of the digestive tract in meters: _____

Analysis Questions:

1-How does the length of your digestive system compare to your height?

_____

2-How is your digestive system able to fit inside your abdomen?

_____

3-Why does the digestive system need to be so long?

_____

_____

4-The longest part of the digestive system is the _____

5-All of the folds in the digestive system and, in particular, the small intestine provide a lot of surface area. Explain the relationship between surface area and nutrient absorption.

_____

_____

Write the letter of the word that best matches the description below. Answers with number after them are used more than once.

A. Anus
B. Appendix
C. Esophagus
D. Gallbladder
E. Large Intestines (Colon)

F. Liver
G.Villi
H. Mouth (Oral cavity) (2)
I. Pancreas
J. Pharynx

K. Rectum
L. Salivary Glands
M. Small intestine (4)
N. Stomach (2)
O. Tongue

_____6. Stores bile until it is secreted.

_____7. Produces/makes bile.

_____8. Two anatomical regions where mechanical digestion occurs.

_____9. Organ that mixes food in the mouth.

_____10. Common passage for food and air.

_____11. Literally a food chute; it has no digestive or absorptive role.

_____12. Organ where carbohydrate chemical digestion begins.

_____13.Produces a juice that neutralizes stomach acid and contains digestive enzymes.

_____14. Organ responsible for absorption of most nutrients.

_____15. Organ primarily involved in water absorption and feces formation.

_____16. Pouch with hangs from the initial part of the colon.

_____17. Organ in which protein chemical digestion begins.

_____18. Produce enzymes that begin carbohydrate digestion.

_____19. Organ that receives pancreatic juice and bile.

_____20. Opening through which feces are expelled from the body.

_____21. Stores feces until they are excreted.

_____22. Organ into which the stomach empties.

_____23. Fingerlike extensions in the intestinal wall that increase surface area.

_____24. Organ where most lipid chemical digestion occurs.

Excretory System: Kidney and Nephron

<u>Materials</u>: Colored pencils

The basic structural and functional unit of the kidney is the nephron. Each kidney has about 1 million nephrons, all packed into an area of the kidney called the cortex. The nephron's primary function is to filter blood, but as you can see from the diagram, this is not a simple process. The nephron has three major parts: the glomerulus, the Bowman's Capsule, and the tubule (which is further divided into the proximal and distal tubule and the Loop of Henle).

Blood enters the kidney from the renal artery and moves into the glomerulus, where filtration occurs. Filtration is the process by which water and dissolved particles are pulled out of the blood. The resulting liquid, called filtrate, contains water and many of the toxic substances that might have accumulated in the blood (like ammonia). The glomerulus is enclosed by the Bowman's capsule, small molecules and water can pass through this area, but larger molecules do not. The filtrate is then collected in the Bowman's capsule for transport through the nephron.

The nephron itself will restore vital nutrients and water back into the blood, while retaining the waste products the body needs to eliminate. Two processes accomplish this task: tubular reabsorption and tubular secretion. During tubular reabsorption, cells in the proximal tubule remove water and nutrients from the filtrate and pass them back into the blood, wastes such as urea are retained in the tubule. During tubular secretion, wastes that were not initially filtered out in the bowman's capsule are removed from the blood in the distal tubule. Ammonia and many drugs are removed from the blood during tubular secretion.

The concentrated filtrate moves into the proximal tubule. Notice the capillaries that wrap around the tubules. At the points of contact with the tubule and the capillaries, water and nutrients are reabsorbed into the blood. In addition, wastes remaining in the blood after filtration are passed to the tubule. The filtrate flows from the proximal tubule and into the Loop of Henle. The Loop of Henle concentrates the filtrate, by removing more water from it, and passes it to the distal tubule. From the distal tubule it travels to the collecting duct. The filtrate is now called urine. The collecting duct prepares the urine for transport out of the body. It is collected in the renal pelvis where it eventually enters the ureter. From there it goes to the bladder.

Meanwhile, the blood capillaries that are twisted around the nephron join back to the renal vein. From there, the blood travels to the posterior vena cava, eventually reaching the heart.

As you can see, the blood passes through many structures in a nephron and there are many nephrons in our two kidneys. All those nephrons provide lots of surface area for maximum reabsorption of water and nutrients, as well as removal of toxins from our blood.

Coloring-Coding Instructions

A. Color the renal artery red. The blood continues through the smaller arteries and into the glomerulus and then out again (like a tangled ball of yarn). The renal artery continues down the "left" side of the nephron.

B. Color the renal vein dark blue and follow it through the smaller venules. The renal vein continues down the "right" side of the nephron.

C. The arterioles(red) and the venules (blue) will meet somewhere in the center and at the Loop of Henle. Color the part where they meet, the capillaries, purple.

D. Color the proximal tubule dark green, until it reaches the Loop of Henle. The Loop of Henle should be colored dark pink. When the Loop of Henle becomes the distal tubule, color the distal tubule light green.

E. Color the Bowman's capsule brown. Leave the glomerulus uncolored. (You should have already colored the arteries inside it red.)

F. Color both the collecting duct and the ureter yellow.

G. Color the medulla light blue. Color the cortex light pink, and shade the renal pelvis with your regular (#2) pencil. Trace the nephron pictured on the kidney with orange.

Structure of the Kidney and Nephron

Kidney

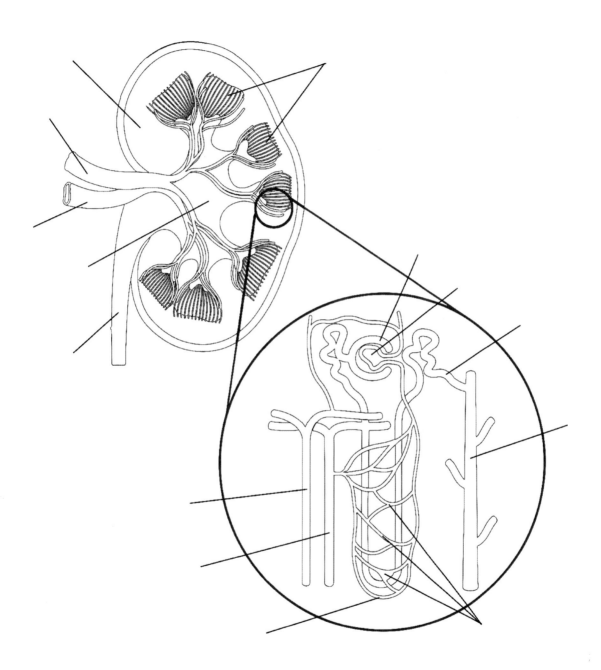

Nephron

Comprehension Questions

1. What is a nephron?

_____

_____

_____

2. What are the 3 parts of a nephron and their purposes?

_____

_____

_____

_____

_____

_____

3. Starting with the renal artery, list all the structures that the filtrate (urine) will pass through before it exists the body.

_____

_____

_____

_____

_____

_____

_____

4-How many nephrons are in a kidney?

_____

5-The nephron restores vital _____ and _____ back into the blood, while

retaining the _____ products the body needs to eliminate.

6-After the urine is collected in the collecting duct and moved into the renal pelvis, where does it go?

_____

_____

7-How many kidneys are in the human body? (check your notes).

_____

8-Label this diagram:

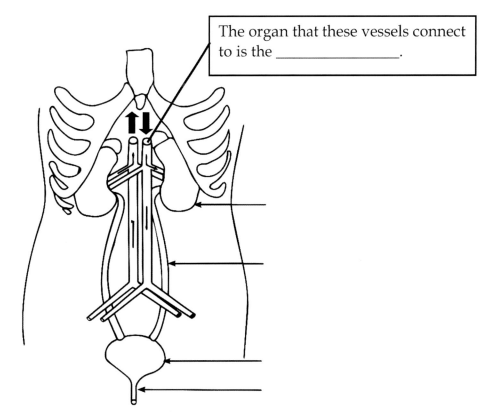

The organ that these vessels connect to is the _____.

Name_____ Date_____ Period_____ Lab_____

Nervous System

Use the following information to help you color-code the diagrams that follow.

A NEURON:

The nervous system includes senses, the ability to think and act, as well as involuntary responses (like heart rate and breathing rate). Neurons are the basic functional units of the nervous system. They generate electrical signals called action potentials, which allow them to quickly transmit information over long distances.

Neurons, like other cells, have a cell body (called the soma). The nucleus of the neuron is found in the soma. Label the nucleus (E) and color it RED. Label the soma/cell body (D) and color it BLUE.

Various processes (appendages or protrusions) extend from the cell body. Around one end of the cell body are many small, branching protrusions called dendrites. Neurons receive incoming information through their dendrites. Incoming signals can be either excitatory (making the neuron fire) or inhibitory (keeping the neuron from firing). Label the dendrites (F) and color them BLACK.

Extending from the other end of the cell body is the axon, a long, thin, tube-like protrusion. Label the axon (C) and color it PURPLE. The axon is wrapped in myelin, which is produced by Schwann cells. The myelin covers some sections of the axon, but leaves some sections bare between the sheathed portions. This periodic gap between the myelin facilitates rapid conduction of nerve impulses. Label one of the myelin sheathes (B) and color them ORANGE. Label one of the unsheathed areas of the axon (BB) NODE OF RENVIER.

At its far end, the axon splits up into many axon terminals. Each of these axon terminals forms a synapse with a dendrite of another neuron. Label the axon terminals (A) and color them GREEN.

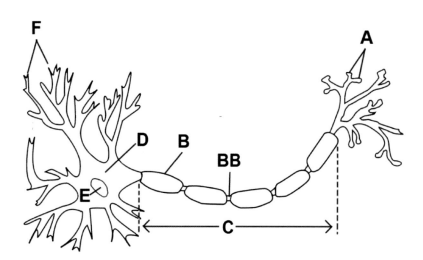

A _____

B _____

BB _____

C _____

D _____

E _____

F _____

NEUROTRANSMISSION:

The axon terminal through which a message is sent belongs to the presynaptic cell; the dendrite which receives the message belongs to the postsynaptic cell. There is a space between the two cells, which is called the synaptic cleft. When an action potential arrives at the axon terminal (of a presynaptic cell), it triggers the release of a neurotransmitter. The neurotransmitter diffuses into the synaptic cleft and binds to receptors on the membrane (dendrites) of the postsynaptic cell.

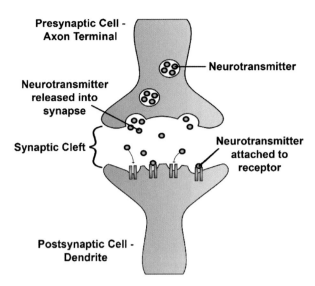

1-How does the neurotransmitter move from one cell to another?

_____

_____

_____

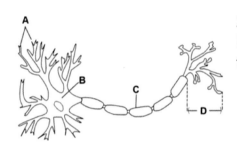

2-The diagram shows a neuron of the nervous system. Which letter shows a structure that releases a substance that crosses the synapse?

1. A   3. C

2. B   4. D

3-The diagram below shows a neuron. A stimulus is detected in the dendrites. Label the location of the dendrites.

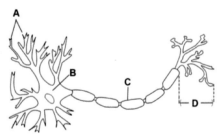

4-A change in the environment that initiates the transmission of an electrochemical charge along a neuron is known as

1. a reflex   3. an impulse

2. a response   4. a stimulus

5-Which substances are secreted at the endings of nerve cells?

    1. antibodies   3. neurotransmitters

    2. antigens   4. lipids

6-When leg muscles respond to a stimulus by moving the foot, the response depends most directly on the functioning of

    1. bronchioles 3. capillaries

    2. nephrons   4. nerves

Base your answer to the question on the diagram below, illustrating one type of cellular communication occurs through nerve cells, and on your knowledge of biology.

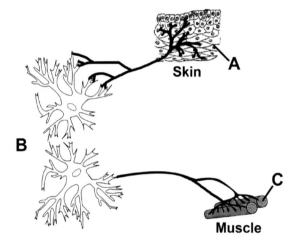

7-State *one* possible cause for the failure of muscle *C* to respond to a stimulus at *A*.

_____

_____

The Brain

Neurons transmit signals to and from the brain. In terms of size, some neurons are small, but others are quite large. Many neurons extend from the brain to the spinal cord and others extend from various places in the body to the brain stem. The brain, itself, is divided into areas which perform different functions. Descriptions of important brain structures follow:

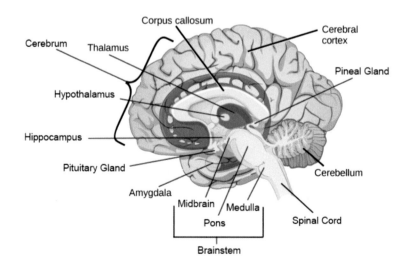

Occipital lobe: This is found in the back of the brain. The area is involved with the brain's ability to recognize objects. It is responsible for vision.

Temporal lobes: The temporal lobes are found on either side of the brain, above the ears. They are responsible for hearing, memory, meaning, and language, as well as play a role in emotion, learning, and processing auditory stimuli.

Parietal lobes: The parietal lobes are found behind the frontal lobes, above the temporal lobes, and at the top back of the brain. They are responsible for the processing of nerve impulses related to the senses, such as touch, pain, taste, pressure, and temperature. They also have language functions.

Frontal lobe: It is concerned with emotions, reasoning, planning, movement, and speech. It is also involved in creativity, judgment, problem solving, and planning

Cerebral Cortex/Cerebrum: Controls thinking, voluntary movements, language, reasoning, and perception. In higher mammals the cortex has lots of wrinkles, grooves and bumps.

Cerebellum: Controls movement, balance, posture, and coordination. New research has also linked it to thinking, novelty, and emotions.

Limbic system: A set of brain structures located on both sides of the thalamus, immediately beneath the cerebrum. It supports a variety of functions including emotion, behavior, motivation, long-term memory, and olfaction (the sense of smell).

Hypothalamus: Controls body temperature, emotions, hunger, thirst, appetite, digestion and sleep. The hypothalamus is composed of several different areas and is located at the base of the brain.

Thalamus: Controls sensory and motor integration. Receives sensory information and relays it to the cerebral cortex. Transmits information received from the cerebrum to other parts of the brain.

Pituitary gland: Controls hormones and helps turn food into energy.

Pineal gland: Controls growth and maturation. It is activated by light.

Amygdala: The amygdala controls your emotions.

Hippocampus: Forms and stores your memories. (Scientists think there are other things unknown about the hippocampus). It is involved in learning. People with Alzheimer's disease loose the functioning of their hippocampus.

Midbrain: Controls breathing, reflexes, and swallowing. Includes the Thalamus, Hippocampus, and Amygdala. Every living thing must have a mid-brain.

Pons- Part of the hindbrain. It is involved in motor control and sensory analysis. Some structures within the pons are linked to the cerebellum and are involved in movement and posture.

Medulla Oblongata- This is the caudal-most part (posterior) of the brain stem, between the pons and spinal cord. It maintains vital body functions, such as breathing and heartrate.

Corpus Callosum- Allows communication between the two hemispheres of the brain. It is responsible for transmitting neural messages between both the right and left hemispheres.

Spinal Cord- This is a complex cylinder of nerves that starts at the base of your brain and runs down the vertebral canal. It and the brain are part of the body's central nervous system. Electrical currents travel up and down the spinal cord, sending signals which allow different segments of the body to communicate with the brain. The spinal cord allows for coordinated movements while walking and involuntary responses to stimuli, called reflexes.

Use this information (and your notes) to help you fill in the blanks that follow.

The Brain

Label the parts of the CNS on the diagram below. Give the purpose/function of each part.

a. cerebellum - _____

b. medulla oblongata - _____

c. thalamus - _____

d. hypothalamus - _____

e. corpus callosum - _____

f. pons - _____

g. spinal cord - _____

h. cerebrum - _____

i. pituitary gland - _____

j. Label the parts of the brain

k. Lobes of the Cerebrum

The diagram below shows the four lobes of each hemisphere of the cerebrum: frontal, parietal, occipital and temporal. Label each lobe. Then complete the fill-in below.

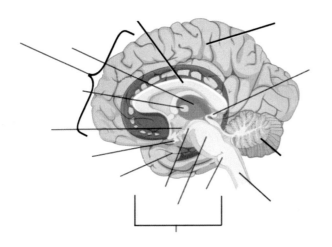

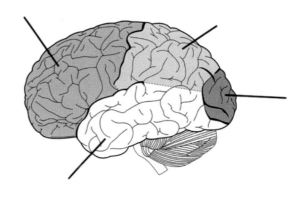

l-The _____ lobes control some body movements, reasoning, judgment and

emotions. The sense of vision is in the _____ lobe. The sense of hearing is

interpreted in the _____ lobes. The _____ lobes interpret

sensations such as pain, pressure, touch, hot and cold.

Understanding Viruses

There are thousands of kinds of viruses. Most consist only of tiny particles of genetic material surrounded by a coat of protein and sometimes an outer envelope. Specific viruses attach themselves to the outsides of specific host cells, and then work their way inside through the host's outer membranes. Once inside their host cells, the viruses reproduce. The new viruses can destroy their host cells and then move on to attack new host cells. Shown below are some examples of viruses.

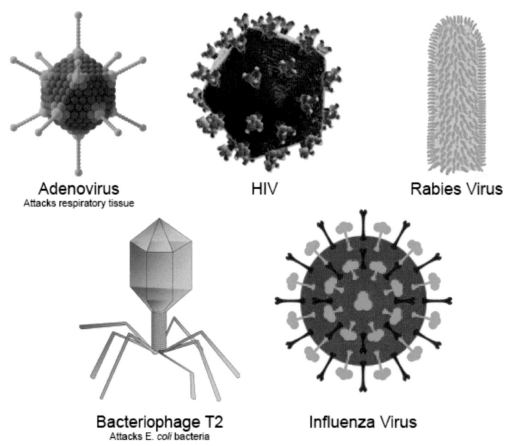

Adenovirus
Attacks respiratory tissue

HIV

Rabies Virus

Bacteriophage T2
Attacks E. *coli* bacteria

Influenza Virus

In humans, **Macrophages** are the first line of defense against viruses and other pathogens. They are white blood cells that engulf foreign substances. Macrophages alone, however, can seldom defend the body. After eating a pathogen, a macrophage signals the lymphocytes for help.

Lymphocytes are part of the immune system. Very often, they are T or B cells or NK (natural killer) cells. A **lymphocyte** can recognize an invader only by its **shape**. To help you to learn how lymphocytes do this, the shape of a typical virus is described here.

Since the **phage virus** (or bacteriophage) has an easy shape to understand, it will be our example. It is important for you to know that this virus is **harmless** to humans. Its tail fibers allow it to land only on bacteria and archaea cells.

Description of Phage Virus/Bacteriophage:

1. The virus is a very small **particle**. Because it acts like a nonliving particle most of the time, scientists are not sure whether it should be classified as a living or a non-living substance. The diagram below shows a typical virus. On the **title line**, write "**A Typical Virus.**"

2. The body of the virus looks more like a **crystal** than like living **tissue**. This crystal-like structure is called the "envelope." Arrow A points to the envelope. Find **arrow A** and label it "**envelope.**" Use RED to color the envelope.

3. Inside the envelope is a **genetic strand** (DNA or RNA). It has a chemical code that orders an attacked cell to make more viruses. Arrow B points to the genetic strand. Label **arrow B** "**genetic strand.**" Use BLUE to trace the genetic strand.

4. To inject the genetic strand into a cell, the virus uses a **needlelike structure** called the "**tail sheath.**" Arrow C points to the tail sheath. Find **arrow C** and label it "**tail sheath.**" Use GREEN to color the tail sheath.

5. The tail fibers act like **landing gear** and help the virus to **land on a cell**. Arrow D points to the tail fibers. Find **arrow D** and label it "**tail fibers.**" Use PURPLE to color the tail fibers.

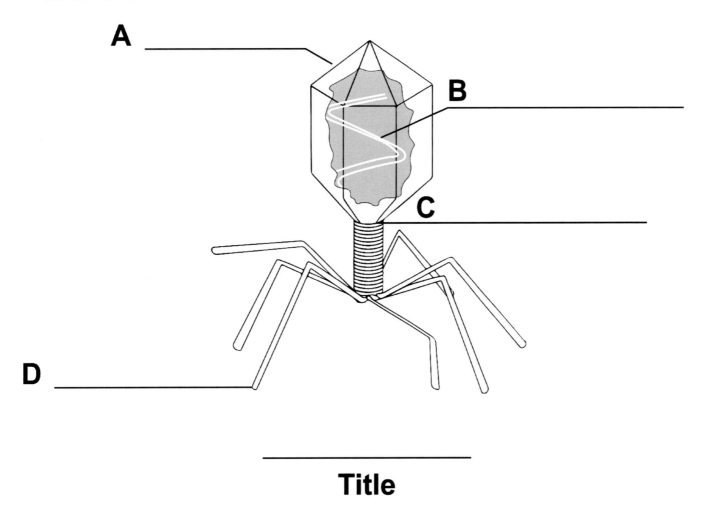

Title

149

Reading Comprehension Fill In:

1-A lymphocyte can recognize an invader by its _____.

2-Scientists are not sure whether viruses should be classified as a living or non-living substance because viruses act like a _____ most of the time.

3-The body (envelope) of the virus looks more like a _____than like living_____.

4-The _____ is located inside the envelope of a virus.

5-A virus uses its _____ _____ to inject its genetic strand into a cell.

6-The tail fibers help the virus to _____

Think About Viruses

7-Explain why the bacteriophage virus can't harm humans.

_____

_____

How Viruses Take Over Human Cells

A virus has no specialized structures for locomotion. It can't swim, walk, or fly; it enters an organism merely by chance. A person can become infected with the flu virus if, for example, they happen to be near an ill person who sneezes or coughs. Some viruses are transmitted by casual contact such as shaking hands, hugging, or kissing. Other viruses can be transmitted from dirty dishes and by animal bites; still others are transmitted only by sexual contact or hypodermic needles.

Even after a virus enters an organism, it must drift along until, by chance, it finds a cell that it can land on. Once it does, a human pathogenic virus partially sinks into a "host" cell. It does this by tricking the "host" cell into thinking the virus is something it needs.

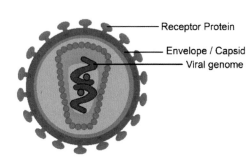

Example of Human Pathogenic Virus

Receptor Protein
Envelope / Capsid
Viral genome

Normally, cells allow nutrients through specially shaped membrane receptors that fit precisely. Viruses have a capsid with receptor proteins that look like nutrients the cell needs. When the virus receptor binds to the cell receptor, the cell thinks the virus is a nutrient, and pulls it in. (Human pathogenic viruses don't have tail sheathes to inject their genetic codes like bacteriophages).

Once the virus is inside the cell, the cell is infected! The virus's genetic material passes through the cell's cytoplasm and into the nucleus. Once in the nucleus, the virus's genetic material combines with the host cell's DNA. The infected cell then becomes a "virus factory." Instead of sending instructions that direct the cell's own normal activities, the virus's genetic material reprograms the host cell's nucleus to send instructions for making new viruses. The cell membrane buds out or is destroyed as new viruses escape to infect other cells, repeating the infection cycle.

8- Use the Example of the Human Pathogenic Virus on above to help you label another human pathogenic virus below. Identify the following parts of the virus: RECEPTOR PROTEINS, CAPSID (ENVELOPE), GENETIC MATERIAL.

Virus

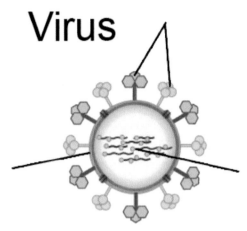

Reading Comprehension

9-If viruses don't have a means of locomotion; how do they get from one place to another?

_____

_____

10-How do viruses "trick" cells?

_____

_____

11-When is a cell said to be infected?

_____

_____

12-Why is an infected cell called a "virus factory"?

_____

_____

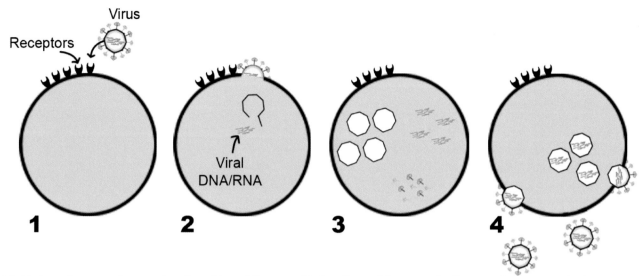

13-Using the reading selection How Viruses Take Over Human Cells, explain what is happening in each of the steps 1-4.

Step 1:

_____

_____

_____

Step 2:

_____

_____

_____

Step 3:

_____

_____

_____

Step 4:

_____

_____

_____

Reproduction & Development

Name_____ **Date**_____ **Period**_____ **Lab**_____

Diagramming Embryological Development

<u>Materials</u>: Scissors, tape or glue stick

Embryological development begins at <u>conception</u> when the sperm and egg cell unite in one of the two fallopian tubes. As the single-celled <u>zygote</u> moves toward the uterus (taking 3-5 days), it begins the process called cleavage. *During cleavage the zygote first divides into two cells, then into four, eight, and so on. As the cells divide, they get smaller, so the 32-cell solid ball stage (known as the <u>morula</u>) is the same size as the zygote.*

1-Conception signals the start of

_____

2-The sperm and egg unit to form a

_____

3-The process of the zygote's cells dividing, yet not getting any bigger is called

_____

4-Once the zygote is a solidly packed ball of cells it is called a

_____

When the morula develops a hollow, fluid-filled space it is called a <u>blastula</u> (in humans, <u>blastocyst</u>). This occurs at approximately day 5. By day 7, the blastocyst attaches to the endometrium (uterine lining). At this point, the cells of the blastocyst are <u>pluripotent</u> (stem cells), meaning they can turn into the cells of any body tissue.

5-In humans, a blastocyst is formed when the morula forms a fluid-filled space. The cells of the blastocyst, morula, and zygote were all pluripotent, meaning than can g_____ into any kind of body tissue.

Along with the developing life, two cavities form within the fluid-filled space of the blastocyst. The first cavity will eventually become the <u>placenta</u>, an organ which carries oxygen and nutrients from mother to the new life and waste materials from the new life to mother. The second cavity will become the <u>amniotic sac</u>, which provides a space where the life can grow.

6-The developing blastocyst needs two important structures as it burrows into the endometrium of the uterus. Those structures are:

_____

_____

7-The purpose of the placenta is

_____

_____

8-The purpose of the amniotic sac is

_____

_____

When the blastocyst attaches to the woman's uterus it is known as implantation. Implantation occurs when the cells nestle into the endometrium and rupture tiny blood vessels. Implantation fails about fifty percent of the time. When successful, the connective web of blood vessels and membranes between the blastocyst and uterus is usually completed by day 9 or 10.

Meanwhile, during days 7-10, a major cellular reorganization occurs where three germ (tissue) layers are formed in a process called gastrulation. Now called the gastrula, its layers are the ectoderm (which will become the skin and nervous system), the endoderm (which will become the digestive and respiratory systems), and the mesoderm (which will become the muscle and skeletal systems). These new cellular layers contain differentiated cells, which perform specialized jobs within the gastrula. (They are no longer pluripotent).

9-Gastrulization is an important milestone because this is when the cells of the developing life become differentiated. Explain how this is different from the previous stages of embryonic development.

_____

_____

_____

_____

To maintain the pregnancy, the placenta produces several hormones. Among them is human chorionic gonadotropin (HCG), which prevents the ovaries from releasing eggs and stimulates the ovaries to produce estrogen and progesterone continuously. To protect the developing embryo, the amniotic sac, which forms by day 12, is filled with amniotic fluid in which the developing embryo floats.

10-Chemical signals called _____ are necessary to maintain the pregnancy.

11-Other species, like fish and amphibians, can't do internal fertilization. Identify the structure that enables humans to do internal fertilization and explain why it is necessary.

_____

_____

_____

_____

Neurulation occurs during weeks 3-6. This is the formation of the neural tube in which cells in an area of the ectoderm called the neural plate grow, invaginate (move inward), and pinch off from the surface to form a hollow tube. The neural tube eventually develops into the central nervous system including the brain and spinal cord.

After the ectoderm (skin/nervous system) forms the neural tube, the mesoderm (muscle/skeletal) and endoderm (digestive/respiratory) follow. Ultimately, the body contains an inner tube (digestive tract) with a series of tubes that wrap around it. In this way, the three germ layers all contribute to the developing embryo.

12-As the blastocyst develops into an independent human, its germ layers mature into three interconnected tubes. They are the

_____

_____

_____

13-Identify what each of the germ layers eventually develops into:

Ectoderm:

_____

Mesoderm:

_____

Endoderm:

_____

Once the major body systems are in place, the embryo begins the development of some external physical features. In the fourth week it has a head with eyes, nose, ears, and mouth. The cardiovascular system is where the earliest activity begins as the blood vessel that will become the heart starts to pulse.

During the fifth week (counted from the first day of the woman's last menstrual period), buds that will form the arms and legs appear. By the time the eighth week of development has been reached, the embryo has all of the basic organs and parts except those of the sex organs. At this point, the embryo weighs just one gram and is about one inch in length.

At 8 weeks after fertilization (10 weeks of pregnancy), the end of the embryonic period, the basic structures of the brain and central nervous system have been established. As neurons form, they migrate to different areas of the brain. Once they have reached the correct location, they begin to form connections with other neural cells, establishing rudimentary neural networks.

At the end of the 8th week after fertilization (10 weeks of pregnancy), the embryo is considered a fetus. During this stage, the structures that have already formed grow and develop. Important milestones of pregnancy include: the fetus filling the entire uterus by 12 weeks, sex identification by 14 weeks, at 16-20 weeks pregnant women can feel the fetus moving, and by 24 weeks (6 months) the fetus has a chance of survival outside the uterus. The lungs continue to mature until near the time of delivery. The brain accumulates new cells throughout pregnancy and the first year of life after birth.

14-Eight weeks after fertilization the developing life is no longer an _____, it is now called

a _____.

15-After two months (eight weeks) there is still much growth and development to be done. The process of cell division after conception and for the rest of life will be done through the process of m_____. The only part of the body that does meiosis are the

_____

16-A full term baby is one that gestates for 9 months. If it is born prematurely, its best chance of survival is if it is delivered after at least _____ months.

Cut out the 7 cells on the last page of this lab. These cells represent changes that occur in the developing life during its first week. The italicized sections on the 1st page of this lab describe the process of development from zygote to morula to blastocyst. Place the 7 cells on the appropriate locations on the Fertilization and Implantation Diagram.

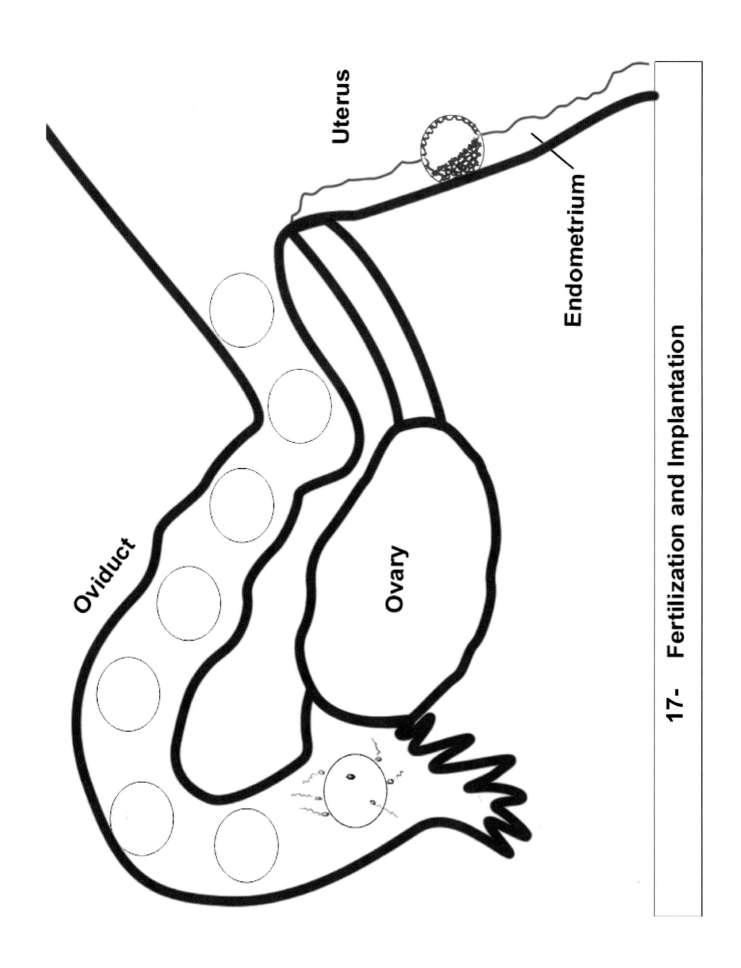

Uterus

Endometrium

Oviduct

Ovary

17- Fertilization and Implantation

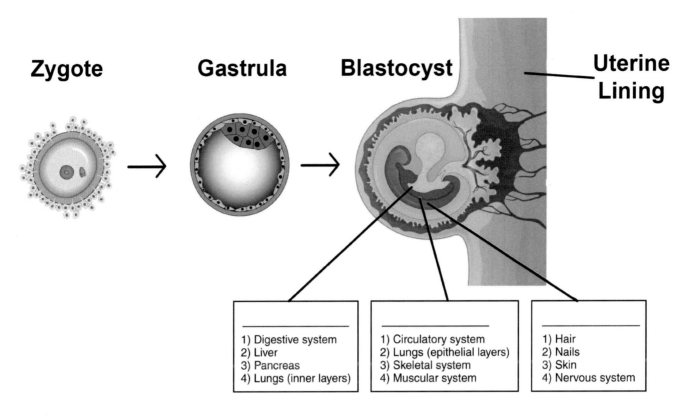

Zygote   **Gastrula**   **Blastocyst**   **Uterine Lining**

_____
1) Digestive system
2) Liver
3) Pancreas
4) Lungs (inner layers)

_____
1) Circulatory system
2) Lungs (epithelial layers)
3) Skeletal system
4) Muscular system

_____
1) Hair
2) Nails
3) Skin
4) Nervous system

18- **Label the Germ Layers above**

The zygote, morula, and blastocyst are made of pluripotent cells; The gastrula, embryo and fetus are made of differentiated cells.

19- Explain the difference below.

_____

_____

_____

_____

_____

_____

_____

_____

_____

_____

Cut out these 7 cells. These cells represent changes that occur in the developing life during its first week. The italicized sections on the 1st page of this lab describe the process of development from zygote to morula to blastocyst. Place the 7 cells on the appropriate locations on the Fertilization and Implantation Diagram.

Diagramming Meiosis

Mitosis is used for almost all of your body's (somatic) cell division needs. It adds new cells during development and replaces old and worn-out cells throughout your life. The goal of mitosis is to produce daughter cells that are genetically identical to their mothers, with not a single chromosome more or less.

Meiosis, on the other hand, is used for just one purpose in the human body: the production of gametes—sex cells, or sperm and eggs. Its goal is to make daughter cells with exactly half as many chromosomes as the starting cell.

To put that another way, meiosis in humans is a division process that takes us from a diploid cell—one with two sets of chromosomes—to haploid cells—ones with a single set of chromosomes. This is why meiosis is sometimes called reduction division. In humans, the haploid cells made in meiosis are sperm and eggs (gametes). When a sperm and an egg join in fertilization, the two haploid sets of chromosomes form a complete diploid set: a new genome.

1-What is the difference between somatic cells and sex cells?

_____

_____

_____

2-The goal of mitosis is

_____

_____

3-The goal of meiosis is

_____

4-Mitosis produces d_____ cells; meiosis produces h_____ cells.

5-Sperm and eggs are s_____ cells or g_____ cells.

The basic number of chromosomes in the somatic cells of a species is called the somatic number and is labelled 2n. In humans 2n = 46: we have 46 chromosomes. In the sex cells the chromosome number is n (humans: n = 23). So, in normal diploid organisms, chromosomes are present in two copies, one from each parent (23x2=46). The only exception are the sex chromosomes. In mammals, the female has two X chromosomes, and the male one X and one Y chromosome.

6-The human diploid number is _____; the human haploid number is _____.

In many ways, meiosis is a lot like mitosis. The cell goes through similar stages and uses similar strategies to organize and separate chromosomes. In meiosis, however, the cell has a more complex task. It still needs to separate sister chromatids (the two halves of a duplicated chromosome), as in mitosis. But it must also separate homologous chromosomes, the similar but nonidentical chromosome pairs an organism receives from its two parents.

These goals are accomplished in meiosis using a two-step division process. Homologue pairs separate during a first round of cell division, called meiosis I. Sister chromatids separate during a second round, called meiosis II.

Since cell division occurs twice during meiosis, one starting cell can produce four gametes (eggs or sperm). In each round of division, cells go through four stages: prophase, metaphase, anaphase, and telophase.

7-How are mitosis and meiosis alike?

_____

_____

8-During meiosis sister _____ are separated, as are h_____ chromosomes.

Meiosis "mixes and matches" genes. The gametes produced in meiosis are all haploid, but they're not genetically identical. Each gamete has a unique "sample" of the genetic material present in the starting cell.

Gametes will be genetically different because homologous pairs randomly orient which produces great genetic diversity. Another reason gametes are genetically different from each other is crossing-over. Crossing-over is when homologues exchange genetic material. This also occurs randomly so that each cell that goes through meiosis will be different.

All eukaryotes that reproduce sexually use meiosis. This also includes many single-celled organisms. Meiosis does not occur in archaea or bacteria, which reproduce by asexual processes such as binary fission.

9-Meiosis is different from mitosis in that the daughter cells that are produced are not

i_____.

10-Gametes are genetically different from each other because of random sorting of homologous

pairs and c_____-o_____ of genetic material between homologous

chromosomes.

Using a textbook or other resource fill out the Meiosis Table (sexual reproduction).

11-What are homologous chromosomes?

_____

_____

12-What does it mean to be diploid?

_____

13-What does it mean to be haploid?

_____

14-How many cells are there at the end of Meiosis II? _____

Are they haploid or diploid? _____

15-How does meiosis lead to increased genetic variation?

_____

_____

16-How would the gametes be affected if a pair of chromatids failed to separate in the second meiotic division?

_____

_____

_____

_____

Meiosis / Sexual Reproduction Table

Picture	Phase	Key Points- What Happens

Observing the Cell Cycle in Onion Root Tips

<u>Materials</u>: Scissors, tape or glue stick

The cell cycle is the process by which cells grow and divide. In eukaryotic cells, this process includes a series of four distinct phases. Gap 1 phase (G 1), Synthesis phase (S), and Gap 2 phase (G 2) of the cell cycle are collectively referred to as <u>interphase</u>. The fourth phase, Mitosis (M) involves the division of the cell nucleus.

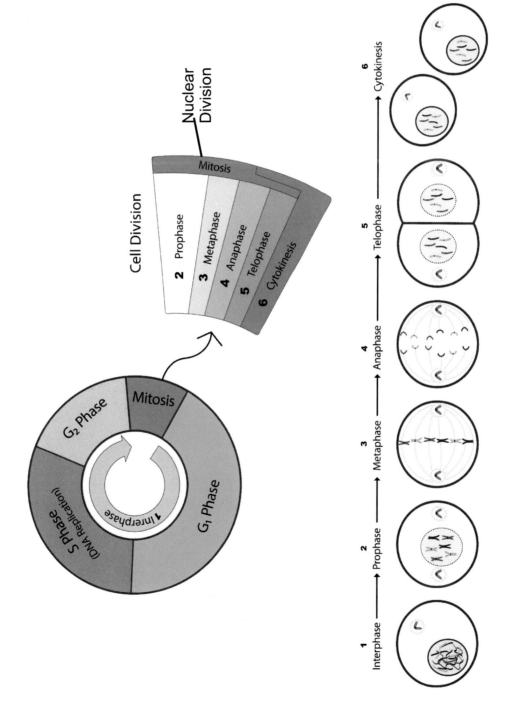

Cells spend 90-95% of their time in interphase in preparation for mitosis. During interphase, cells increase in mass and replicate DNA. During mitosis, nuclear chromosomes separate and then cytokinesis (division of the cytoplasm) occurs. At the end of the mitotic cell cycle, two distinct daughter cells are produced. Each cell contains identical genetic material.

The time it takes for a cell to complete one cell cycle varies depending on the type of cell. In humans, blood cells in bone marrow, skin cells, and cells lining the stomach and intestines, divide rapidly and constantly. Other cells divide when needed to replace damaged or dead cells. These cell types include cells of the kidneys, liver, and lungs. Still other cell types, including nerve cells, stop dividing once mature.

During mitosis and cytokinesis, the contents of the dividing cell are equally distributed between two daughter cells. Mitosis has four phases: Prophase, Metaphase, Anaphase, and Telophase.

Prophase: Changes occur in both the cytoplasm and nucleus of the dividing cell. The chromatin condenses into chromosomes. The chromosomes begin to migrate toward the cell center. The nuclear envelope breaks down and spindle fibers form at opposite poles of the cell.

Metaphase: The nuclear membrane disappears completely. The spindle fully develops, and the chromosomes align at the equatorial plate. (Chromosomes Meet in the Middle).

Anaphase: Paired chromosomes (sister chromatids) separate and begin moving to opposite ends (poles) of the cell. (Chromosomes are pulled Apart). Spindle fibers not connected to chromatids lengthen and elongate the cell.

Telophase: Chromosomes are within two distinct nuclei; the genetic content is divided equally into two parts.

Cytokinesis, the division of the cytoplasm, begins prior to the end of mitosis and completes shortly after telophase.

Once a cell has completed the mitosis and cytokinesis it goes back into the G 1 phase and repeats the cycle again.

Cells in the body can also be placed in a non-dividing state. Cells may remain in this stage for very long periods until they are signaled to progress through the cell cycle again by growth factors.

When the cell cycle goes wrong, normal cell growth is lost. Cancer cells may develop, which gain control of their own growth signals and continue to multiply unchecked.

In this lab, you will examine the dividing root-tip cells of an onion. You will identify the various phases of the cell cycle. You will answer related analysis questions to further your understanding of the eukaryotic cell cycle.

1-What happens during interphase?

_____

_____

_____

2-What would happen if our cells didn't go through interphase correctly?

_____

_____

3-What would happen if our cells didn't go through mitosis correctly?

_____

_____

4-If you examined cells under a microscope, which phase of the cell cycle would most cells will be in, interphase, mitosis, or cytokinesis? _____ Why?

_____

_____

5-Where in the human body do cells divide fast?

_____

_____

6-Why do the parts of the body mentioned in #5 need to divide fast?

_____

_____

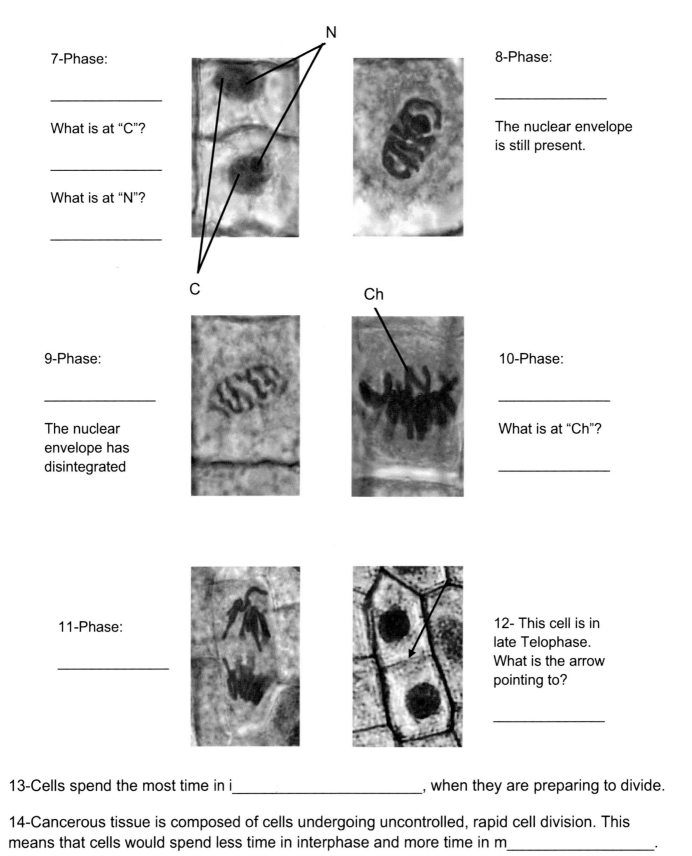

7-Phase:

_____

What is at "C"?

_____

What is at "N"?

_____

N

C

8-Phase:

_____

The nuclear envelope is still present.

Ch

9-Phase:

_____

The nuclear envelope has disintegrated

10-Phase:

_____

What is at "Ch"?

_____

11-Phase:

_____

12- This cell is in late Telophase. What is the arrow pointing to?

_____

13-Cells spend the most time in i_____, when they are preparing to divide.

14-Cancerous tissue is composed of cells undergoing uncontrolled, rapid cell division. This means that cells would spend less time in interphase and more time in m_____.

Onion Tip Cell Cycle Stages Chart

Cut out the diagrams and photographs of the cell cycle stages on the last page of this lab. Match the diagrams and photographs for each of the 6 stages listed on the chart below. Then tape or glue them in the proper location on the chart. Next, complete the chart by describing what is happening in each stage.

Stage	Diagram	Photograph	Description of what's happening in each stage
Interphase			
Prophase			
Metaphase			
Anaphase			
Telophase			
Cytokinesis ➡️ Draw how this would look. (Attach additional paper, if necessary).			

Cut out, match, and tape/glue to Onion Tip Cell Cycle Stages Chart.

Diagrams of Onion Tip Cell Cycle Stages

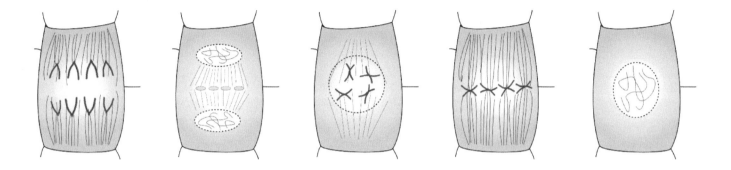

Photographs of Onion Tip Cell Cycle Stages

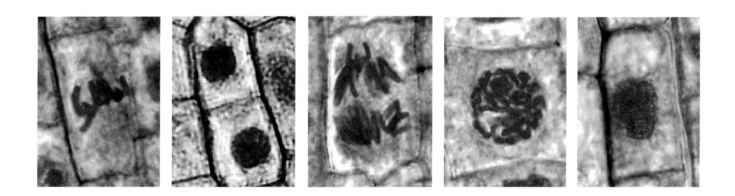

What Limits the Sizes of Cells?

Materials Per Lab Group- 1 hardboiled egg & 1 egg "cube" cut from the white section of egg, dark food coloring (blue), a large beaker, a small beaker, paper towels, metric ruler, and aluminum foil.

Procedure-

A-Place _____ ml of water in large beaker. Place the whole egg in the water. Subtract the volume of water after the egg was added to the beaker from the original volume:

Volume after egg added = _____

Original Volume = _____

The Volume of the egg is = _____

B-Place _____ ml of water in small beaker. Place the egg cube in the water. Subtract the volume of water after the egg cube was added to the beaker from the original volume:

Volume after cube added = _____

Original Volume = _____

The Volume of the cube is = _____

C-Remove the egg and egg cubes from their prospective beakers.

D-Place 200 ml of water in the larger beaker. Add 5 drops of dark food coloring to the beaker. Set aside.

E-Measure the surface area of both the egg and egg cube by wrapping aluminum foil around each (leaving minimal wrinkles and cutting away any overlap). Trace the opened foil shapes onto graph paper. Count the squares to determine the surface area of both the egg and the cube. Count only whole squares.

F-Place both the whole egg and the egg cube in the larger beaker with the food coloring. Allow them to sit until the following day or next class period. (Longer time yields better results).

G-Remove the egg and egg cube from beaker and place on paper towel. Cut both the whole egg and egg cube in half and measure how far the food coloring penetrated with a metric ruler.

Analyze and Conclude-

1-How close to the centers of the egg cube and whole egg did the color reach?

_____

_____

_____

2-Compare the whole egg and the egg cube to cells and explain why a cell can't continue to grow indefinitely. (Use terms like _surface area_ and _volume_).

_____

_____

_____

3- Attach the graph paper with your measurements of surface area and volume. Show the ratio of surface area to volume (SA/Vol) for both the egg and cube.

4-Calculate the surface area, volume, and ratio of surface area to volume of an imaginary cubic cell with a length of 4 cm.

_____

_____

_____

5-Select a cell organelle that we learned about and describe how its functions might be impaired if the cell were to become too large.

_____

_____

_____

Scientific Inquiry

Name_____ Date_____ Period_____ Lab_____

Metric Measurement

If you needed to know the length of a room, you might find the distance in feet. If you were to step on a scale, you would find your weight in pounds. You might measure a quart of milk for a recipe. The foot, pound, and quart are units in the English System.

Scientists, however, use the metric system. In the scientific community, the metric system is known as the International System of Measurement, or SI.

Complete the following charts dealing with metric units and instruments:

Chart 1-

	ENGLISH UNIT	METRIC UNIT
DISTANCE	FOOT	
MASS (WEIGHT)	POUND	
VOLUME	QUART	

Chart 2-

MEASUREMENT	METRIC UNIT	INSTRUMENT USED
DISTANCE		
MASS (WEIGHT)		
VOLUME		

1-Why have scientists adopted the metric system over the English system?

_____

_____

_____

_____

Materials: meter stick and metric ruler, graduated cylinder, beaker, penny, textbooks, balance

Linear Measurement

- Use a meter stick or ruler to measure the following items.
- Place your measurements in the chart below.
- Above each column write the name of the unit that is abbreviated below it.
- Circle the unit you used to directly measure with for each item.
- You will need to convert for the other units.

Chart 3-

Name of Metric Unit				
Diameter of Penny	_____mm	_____cm	_____m	_____km
Length of Parrot Textbook	_____mm	_____cm	_____m	_____km
Width of Dragonfly Textbook	_____mm	_____cm	_____m	_____km
Length of Purple Yarn	_____mm	_____cm	_____m	_____km
Length of Yellow Yarn	_____mm	_____cm	_____m	_____km
Length of Blue Yarn	_____mm	_____cm	_____m	_____km

2-Why should you use a different unit to directly measure a penny compared to the pieces of yarn?

_____

_____

Mass/Weight

Use the balance to measure the mass of the following materials. Place your measurements in the table. Write the name of the unit above the columns below.

Chart 4-

Name of Metric Unit	
Mass of penny	_____ g
Mass of lab tool	_____ g
Mass of empty beaker	_____ g
Mass of beaker with 100 ml of water	_____ g
Mass of 100 ml of water	_____ g

Volume (of liquids)

Use the graduated cylinder to measure the volume of various colored liquids. Place your measurements in the table below along with the name of the metric unit used. Show your teacher for sign off.

Read the meniscus at eye level

Chart 5-

Name of Metric Unit		Teacher Sign-Off
Volume of the red liquid	_____ml	
Volume of the blue liquid	_____ml	
Volume of the green liquid	_____ml	

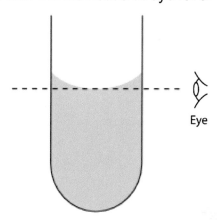
Eye

3-Why are graduated cylinders more accurate measuring devices than beakers?

_____

_____

4-What is a meniscus?

_____

_____

_____

5-Why is it necessary to know about the meniscus when measuring liquids?

_____

_____

_____

6-If moving from a large value to a small value, move the decimal point to the _____

7-When moving the decimal point to the right, we are moving from a _____ value to a

_____ value.

8-What sources of error would account for differences in measurement of the same thing?

_____

_____

9-Which metric measurement would be most useful for measuring the following:

A-Length of an athletic field _____

B-Mass of an aspirin tablet _____

C-Length of a shoe _____

D-Volume of a swimming pool _____

E-Distance from Earth to Mars _____

F-Length of a car _____

G-Mass of a postage stamp _____

Scientific Design—Ethics & Experimenter Bias

Ethics:

Ethics are a set of moral obligations that define right and wrong in our practices and decisions. Many professions have a formalized system of ethical practices that help guide professionals in the field. For example, doctors commonly take the Hippocratic Oath, which, among other things, states that doctors "do no harm" to their patients. In medicine, and in science overall, not making ethical decisions is considered very serious. Failure to make ethical decisions can be punishable by loss of professional license or sometimes punishable by criminal or civil law.

Scientists have long maintained a system of ethics for conducting research, but written guidelines did not develop until the mid-twentieth century. Scientific ethical standards help guide scientific research and ensure that researchers abide by several core principles including:

- Honesty in reporting data
- Careful analysis of results
- Independent analysis and interpretation of results not influenced by external sources
- Open sharing of methods, data, and interpretations through publication and presentation
- Validation and verification of results by repetition and collaboration with peers
- Proper crediting of sources of information, data, and ideas
- Moral obligations to society in general, and, in some disciplines, responsibility in weighing the rights of human and animal subjects

Describe the ethical problem in each of the three historical examples:

In 1951, Dr. Albert M. Kligman, a dermatologist (and future inventor of Retin-A, an acne medicine) began experimenting on inmates at Philadelphia's Holmesburg Prison. Over the next 20 years, prison inmates were used in experiments involving toothpaste, deodorant, shampoo, skin creams, detergents, liquid diets, eye drops, foot powders, and hair dyes. The tests required constant biopsies and painful procedures.

1-Ethical problem:

_____

_____

_____

In 1822, a fur trader in Michigan was accidentally shot in the stomach and treated by Dr. William Beaumont. The fur trader survived — but with a hole in his stomach that never healed. Recognizing the unique opportunity to observe the digestive process, Beaumont began conducting experiments. Beaumont would tie food to a string, then insert it through the hole in the trader's stomach. Every few hours, Beaumont would remove the food to observe how it had been digested. Beaumont's experiments led to the understanding that digestion was a chemical, not a mechanical, process.

2-Ethical problem:

_____

_____

_____

In 1932, the U.S. Public Health Service began working with the Tuskegee Institute to learn about syphilis. Six hundred poor, illiterate, male sharecroppers were found and hired so researchers could observe the progression of untreated syphilis, a STD. None of the men were told they had a life-threatening disease. Instead, they were told they were receiving free healthcare, meals, and burial insurance in exchange for participating. Even after Penicillin was proven an effective cure for syphilis in 1947, the study continued until 1972. In addition to the original subjects, victims of the study included wives who contracted the disease, and children born with congenital syphilis.

3-Ethical problem:

_____

_____

_____

Bias:

When you are given scientific information, it is important to be able to evaluate if the information is accurate. You can investigate the accuracy of scientific information by evaluating whether the conclusions presented are justified based on the experimental design used to collect data.

The following studies all make different claims about the rate of teenage smoking. Each of the studies contains an aspect in its experimental design that might **bias** the results. A bias is a prejudice or opinion in favor of or against a thing, person, or group compared with another, usually in a way considered to be unfair. In science, **research bias** or **experimenter bias**, is a process where the scientists performing the research influence the results to affect the outcome of the experiment in favor of the results they desire.

For the two studies that follow, determine if the **bias** is due to an:
- unrepresentative sample (the group chosen is unlike the rest of the population)
- non-random sample (each member of the population DID NOT have an equal chance of being chosen)
- too small a sample

Then explain how this research bias could affect experimental results.

Experiment 1: Dr. Jackson is making observations at Davisville High School to investigate the rate of smoking among American teenagers. Dr. Jackson decides she will observe students having their lunch in the parking lot where smoking is permitted. Dr. Jackson observes 25 out of 30 students smoking in the parking lot. Based on her observations she records that 83.3% of American teenagers smoke.

4-Research bias due to: _____

This research bias could affect experimental results by

_____

_____

Experiment 2: Dr. Garcia is using both observations and interviews to investigate the rate of smoking among American teenagers. He first selected three study sites: one urban, one rural, and one suburban. Dr. Garcia went to two popular teenage hangouts in each study site and made observations of the teenage students standing around the buildings. He observed a total of 117 students and of those 33 were smoking (28%). Dr. Garcia then went to one high school in each study site and interviewed 25 students from each school. The principal of each school selected the 25 students that would be interviewed for Dr. Garcia's study. Of the 75 total students only 3 said that they smoked regularly (4%). Taking the average percentage from his observations and interviews, Dr. Garcia concluded approximately 16% of American teenagers smoke.

5-Research bias due to: _____

This research bias could affect experimental results by

_____

_____

6-Identify the bias, prejudice, or opinion represented by each of the two groups in the following scenario:

Scenario: A citizen's group, No Butts, has passed around a petition that will make it illegal to have billboard cigarette advertisements in their city. The group claims that billboard cigarette advertisements are often geared at teenagers and that these billboards cause increased smoking rates among teens. No Butts argues that children are especially vulnerable to advertising because they don't have the experience and knowledge to understand and evaluate the purpose of the persuasive advertising. They feel that children cannot differentiate between advertising and other forms of media and cannot tell the difference between reality and fantasy. No Butts says that advertising to children is inherently unfair and deceptive and should be banned.

Newboro Cigarette Company claims that their advertising is not aimed at teenagers and that restricting their advertising will have no effect on the rate of teenage smoking. To demonstrate their point, Newboro Cigarette Company hires Dr. Crestree to conduct a study comparing the smoking rate at schools in towns with cigarette billboard advertising and schools in towns without cigarette billboard advertising. Dr. Crestree goes to three freshman classrooms in areas with and without advertising. These areas are approximately 5 miles apart. Dr. Crestree asks the students to raise their hands if they would answer "yes" to the following questions: Have you ever smoked? Do you smoke every day? Do you smoke once a month or more? The following data was recorded from Dr. Crestree's data collection:

	Schools Without Advertising	Schools with Advertising
Have you smoked?	4%	3.5%
Daily Smoker?	1.3%	1.5%
Monthly Smoker?	2.1%	2%

Because there is no significant difference in the results, Dr. Crestree concludes that the cigarette advertising has no effect on the teenage smoking rate.

A) No Butt's bias:

_____

_____

B) How will their bias affect their message to the public?

_____

_____

C) Newboro Cigarette Company/Dr. Crestree bias:

_____

_____

D) This research bias could affect experimental results by

_____

_____

Scientific Experimentation: Grasshoppers & Heart Medicine

Read the following article and answer the questions that follow.

Two friends, Jim and Tom, wake up from a night of camping with their teammates. The friends then set out to investigate the early morning woods.

As they walk through a meadow of tall grass, Tom notices that the meadow has many active grasshoppers. Jim thinks that the bigger grasshoppers appear to jump three times as far as the smaller ones.

To find out if Jim is correct, both boys collect the grasshoppers and sort them by size. To help them judge the size of the grasshoppers, Tim uses a piece of lined paper he had in his pocket. The boys arrange the grasshoppers into two piles; those which are larger than three lines long on the paper and those which are smaller than three lines long.

Once Jim and Tom finished the sorting, they began to test the notion that big grasshoppers jump three times farther than small ones. Grasshoppers of all sizes were randomly placed one by one on a starting line and prodded once to jump. Tom took off his checkered shirt and placed it on the ground to record how far, in number of checks jumped, the grasshoppers jump.

Their findings showed that ten larger grasshoppers totaled 128 checks, while ten small grasshoppers totaled 57 checks. By this time, Jim and Tom realized that large grasshoppers jumped only twice as far as the small ones.

The two rushed back to camp to tell those who were just awakening about what they had done. However, the boys' teammates, did not believe the figures the boys observed. The rest of the team would only believe the figures with their own eyes. The whole team then went to another field and set up the test as before, except that many more grasshoppers were used. The second set of findings did finally agree with those originally obtained by Jim and Tom, which showed large grasshoppers jumped twice as far as small grasshoppers.

1-The hypothesis of this experiment is

_____

_____

_____

_____

2-List the two (2) instruments that were used.

A) _____

B) _____

3-Describe two ways measurements were taken are:

A) _____

B) _____

4-Give an example of data that was gathered.

_____

5-The results of the experiment were:

_____

_____

6-The conclusion that was drawn based on these results was

_____

_____

7-The conclusion was communicated when

_____

_____

8-The conclusion was verified when

_____

_____

CONDITIONS IN AN EXPERIMENT-Read the article and answer the following questions.

A pharmaceutical company (company that researches, develops, and distributes medicine) sets up the following experiment to test a new heart medication that they have developed:

They advertise for volunteers who suffer from heart disease and separate those who respond into three equal groups.

The volunteers in the first group are given a thorough medical examination and their overall health and the extent of their heart disease are noted. They are given no medication and are told to return in three months for a follow-up examination.

The volunteers in the second group are given a thorough medical examination and the overall health and the extent of their heart disease are noted. They are given a three-month supply of pills made only from flour; however, they are told that they have been given the experimental medication. They are instructed to take one pill a day with their morning meal and to return in three months for a follow-up examination.

The volunteers in the third group are given a thorough medical examination and the overall health and the extent of their heart disease are noted. They are given a three-month supply of the experimental heart medication and they are told that they have been given the experimental medication. They are instructed to take one pill a day with their morning meal and to return in three months for a follow-up examination.

After three months all three groups are brought back and given thorough examinations. Their overall health and the extent of their heart disease are noted.

9-control is a condition of an experiment that does not change and that is used for comparison. Which group of volunteers (1st, 2nd, or 3rd) is the control group? _____

10-A variable is a condition of an experiment that has been changed. Which two groups of volunteers (1st, 2nd, 3rd) contain variables? _____ and _____

11-That group that contains those variables that are specific to, and only to, the intent of the experiment is the experimental group. Which group of volunteers (1st, 2nd, or 3rd) is the experimental group

_____

12-A placebo is a harmless substance given to patients who suspect that it is actually something else. Which group of volunteers (1st, 2nd, or 3rd) received a placebo? _____

Pharmaceutical companies do numerous scientific tests over many years to determine if medication is effective before it is sold to the public. Medication that is highly effective works 95% to 98% of the times it is used by patients.

13-Should a pharmaceutical company continue with their new heart medication experiments based on the following results per 100 volunteers? **Yes / No**

Group	Patients Showing Improvement
Control	53
Placebo	57
Experimental	91

Explain why you think so

_____

_____

_____

14-Should a pharmaceutical company continue with their new heart medication experiments based on the following results per 100 volunteers? **Yes / No**

Group	Patients Showing Improvement
Control	53
Placebo	57
Experimental	58

Explain why you think so:

_____

_____

_____

Scientific Inquiry Questions

15-What is a hypothesis?

_____

16-How is the conclusion of an experiment different than the results of the experiment?

_____

_____

17-What is a control in an experiment?

_____

_____

18-Why is a control necessary in an experiment?

_____

_____

19-What is a variable in an experiment?

_____

_____

20-Why should the number of variables in an experiment be kept to a minimum?

_____

_____

21-What is a placebo?

_____

_____

22-Why would researchers want to include a placebo in an experiment?

_____

_____

_____

Understanding Scientific Inquiry with Butterfly Puddling

Scientists use knowledge and skill when they investigate problems. Their procedures must follow a logical pattern and their conclusions must be evidence based. Although, in practice, scientists work in many ways, one common arrangement of a logical pattern of steps is:

Defining the problem

Forming a h_____ (often referred to as "an educated guess")
Experimentation
Making Observations
Recording and reporting the information
Repeating the experiment
Forming Conclusions

Read the scenario below and answer the questions that follow:

A group of biologists were discussing the clusters of butterflies that seemed to be everywhere around their encampment:

"This evening," said Dr. Samuels, "there were about twenty yellow sulfur butterflies by the stream and some black swallowtails on the manure heap. What are they doing?"

"It's called puddling behavior," replied Dr. Marsh. "You find puddling butterflies in groups in open places such at the edges of drying puddles, or sand bars. I don't think anyone knows what they are doing. Another odd thing is that, in many species, only the males puddle."

Dr. Marsh continued, "An article I read suggested it was a method of population control. Coming together permits the males to count each other. A newcomer can see if there is enough land for him to set up a territory in the area. Puddling saves them having to fight over territories."

"That sounds wrong to me," replied Dr. Gooding. "How can a butterfly figure out the number of males in the area from a group like that? Besides, I've seen swallowtails fight for territories."

"I think it is more likely they're feeding," said Dr. Wells. "It was called 'puddling' in the first place because the butterflies often have their probosces (tongues) out and seem to be sucking something up from the ground."

"I wonder if they are feeding on substances that contain nitrogen. All organisms need nitrogen to make amino acids (the building blocks of proteins). In our lab we've shown that butterfly caterpillars grow faster if you feed them extra nitrogen, and there is lots of nitrogen in a manure pile," said Dr. Gooding.

"But not in sand," came Dr. Marsh's objection "And if they are after nitrogen, you'd expect females to puddle, not males. Females lay the eggs that turn into caterpillars, and extra nitrogen in the egg might be very useful, but it's not the females that puddle."

"It sounds to me," chipped in Dr. Mills, "as if they're after salts that contain sodium. The puddling places contain quite a lot of salts: urine in manure piles and concentrations left by evaporation at the edges of puddles. Animals that feed on plants are short of sodium because plants contain little of it. We put out salt blocks for livestock and end up attracting wildlife as well. Animals need sodium because they lose it in their urine. Male butterflies may need more than females."

In the scenario above the problem was defined and several hypotheses were proposed.
1-What is 'puddling behavior'?

_____

_____

2-What are the three possible hypotheses that were proposed?

_____

_____

_____

Experiments must be designed so that their results are as unambiguous (clear) as possible. For this reason, experiments must include **CONTROL TREATMENTS** as well as **EXPERIMENTAL TREATMENTS**. The two differ only by the factor(s) in which the researcher is interested.

For instance, to test the hypotheses that butterflies puddle for either amino acids or sodium, researchers need to observe butterflies puddling on trays containing amino acids or sodium, but not on control trays that are identical, except that they do not contain amino acids or sodium.

3-Define a 'control' in an experiment:

_____

_____

Doctors Samuels, Marsh, Gooding, Wells, and Mills from the scenario above constructed the following ten trays of five different types:
- 2 trays of dry sand+ sodium chloride solution
- 2 trays of dry sand+ amino acid solution
- 2 trays of dry sand+ sugar solution
- 2 trays of dry sand+ distilled water
- 2 trays of dry sand

4-Identify the three types of experimental trays from the list above:

_____

_____

5-Indentify the two types of control trays from the list above:

_____

_____

Doctors Samuels, Marsh, Gooding, Wells, and Mills designed their experiment so that there would be a large sample size of butterflies. They put their trays in areas where tiger swallowtail butterflies often puddled in large numbers. In each tray they pinned a dead male tiger swallowtail as a decoy because the researchers thought butterflies might be attracted to puddling places by the sight of other butterflies.

When the trays were positioned, the scientists set up a distance out of sight to make observations. Soon dozens of tiger swallowtails were hovering over the trays. Whenever a butterfly landed on a tray, it stuck its proboscis into the sand. On occasion, as many as thirty butterflies were on a tray together. The researchers considered any visit under 15 seconds as a "sampling visit"; Any over 15 seconds was a "puddling visit".

6-What are observations?

_____

7-What is the difference between sampling and puddling?

_____

The scientists were certain that their results would be accurate because they had taken the following precautions: They varied the substances in each location of data collection. Each day, a tray with a different substance was located near the stream, willow tree, huge boulder, swamp, and sunny field. Also, the trays were not labeled as to what substance they contained, so the team recording the butterflies' visits did not know which tray contained which solution, making the experiment 'blind'.

8-Why was it important to move the trays to a different location each day?

_____

_____

9-Why is making an experiment blind important?

_____

_____

The following data were recorded by the researchers:

Day 1

Tray	Sampling	Puddling
1-Dry Sand	26	0
2-Distilled Water	47	1
3-Sugar	60	43
4-Amino Acid	27	206
5-Sodium Chloride	81	403

Day 2

Tray	Sampling	Puddling
1-Dry Sand	48	0
2-Distilled Water	27	1
3-Sugar	25	0
4-Amino Acid	169	304
5-Sodium Chloride	74	321

Day 3

Tray	Sampling	Puddling
1-Dry Sand	52	0
2-Distilled Water	31	2
3-Sugar	27	1
4-Amino Acid	202	408
5-Sodium Chloride	79	436

Day 4

Tray	Sampling	Puddling
1-Dry Sand	55	0
2-Distilled Water	31	2
3-Sugar	30	2
4-Amino Acid	213	422
5-Sodium Chloride	80	429

Day 5

Tray	Sampling	Puddling
1-Dry Sand	53	0
2-Distilled Water	30	3
3-Sugar	35	4
4-Amino Acid	215	425
5-Sodium Chloride	79	422

Compare the sample visits to the puddling visits of trays 1, 2, and 3 for all 5 days of the experiment.
10-Did the number of puddling visits compared to sampling visits of trays 1, 2, and 3 increase or decrease?

_____

Compare the sample visits to the puddling visits of trays 4 and 5 for all 5 days of the experiment.
11-Did the number of puddling visits compared to sampling visits of trays 4 and 5 increase or decrease?

_____

Calculate averages for the puddling visits

	Average
Dry Sand	
Distilled Water	
Sugar	
Amino Acids	
Sodium Chloride	

In the space below construct a BARGRAPH based on the averages of PUDDLING VISITS and TRAY TYPE (ignore sampling visits). BE SURE to: title the graph, construct appropriate scales where needed, label both the x-axis and y-axis, and complete the construction NEATLY!!!

12-Based on the results of the experiment, have the scientists been able to identify ONE reason why certain butterflies puddle?

_____

13-Interpret the graphed data.

_____

_____

14-Some members of the scientific group want to publish the team's findings about why tiger swallowtail butterflies puddle in scientific journals. Explain why this experiment DOES NOT support such an endeavor.

_____

_____

15-What is the ONLY thing that this experiment has shown?

_____

_____

Study of Life

Name_____ Date_____ Period_____ Lab_____

Characteristics of Life: Invertebrates

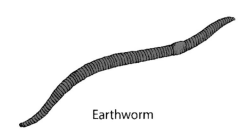
Earthworm

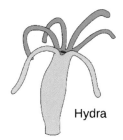
Hydra

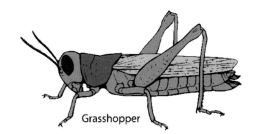
Grasshopper

We can learn more about life functions of animals by studying invertebrate animals such as the hydra, earthworm, and grasshopper.

The **hydra** is a freshwater animal. Its body consists of a thin, tube that measures up to about 30 mm long. The organism is made of two layers of cells and a digestive cavity. The lower end of its body is closed. An opening at the upper end both ingests food and egests its waste. Several tentacles are located around the opening.

Some members of the genus Hydra reproduce by budding, a type of asexual reproduction in which new individuals grow from offshoots from the adult.

Hydra locomotion occurs by a somersaulting motion. The hydra genus is represented by about 25 species. All Hydra species feed on other small invertebrate animals such as crustaceans.

An **earthworm** is a tube-shaped, segmented worm found in the phylum Annelida. Earthworms are commonly found living in soil, feeding on live and dead organic matter. An earthworm's digestive system runs through the length of its body. It conducts respiration through its skin. The earthworm's transport system includes a fluid filled cavity called the coelom (*see-lum*) and a simple, closed blood circulatory system. It has a central and a peripheral nervous system. Muscles all along the worm's body enable it to move.

Earthworms are hermaphrodites—each individual carries both male and female sex organs. They do not have an internal skeleton nor exoskeleton. Rather, they maintain their structure with fluid-filled coelom chambers that function as a hydrostatic skeleton.

Earthworms have the ability to regenerate lost segments, but this ability varies between species and depends on the extent of the damage.

Grasshoppers are insects of the order Orthoptera. At high population densities and under certain environmental conditions, some grasshopper species can change color and behavior and form swarms. Under these circumstances they are known as locusts. Grasshoppers are generally plant-eaters, but are sometimes omnivorous. Swarms of locusts have had dramatic effects that have changed the course of history. Even small numbers grasshoppers can be serious pests. Perhaps surprisingly, in some parts of the world they are eaten as food! They are also featured in art and literature.

Grasshoppers have an extensive set of external sense organs. They have a pair of large compound eyes; a pair of antennae containing olfactory (smell) and touch receptors, and mouthparts containing gustatory (taste) receptors. They also have a pair of tympanal organs for sound reception. There are numerous fine hairs covering their whole body that act as mechanoreceptors (touch and wind sensors). The receptors convey information to the central nervous system through sensory neurons.

Like other insects, grasshoppers have an open circulatory system and their body cavities are filled with a blood-like substance. A heart-like structure pumps the fluid throughout the body. Respiration is performed by valves and muscular pumping of air throughout the body.

Grasshoppers jump by extending their large back legs and pushing against the substrate (the ground, a twig, a blade of grass or whatever else they are standing on); the reaction force propels them into the air. Grasshoppers hatch from eggs and have immature stages in which they molt. They develop an exoskeleton and functional wings.

Complete the following chart using information from this reading, your note packet, and your knowledge of biology. Add paper if necessary:

Life Functions	Hydra	Earthworm	Grasshopper
Environmental Response			
Growth			
Reproduction			
Evolve			
Nutrition			

Life Functions	Hydra	Earthworm	Grasshopper
Homeostasis			
Excretion			
Regulation			
Transport			
Locomotion			

Name_____ Date_____ Period_____ Lab_____

Demonstrating Diffusion & Osmosis: "The Egg Lab"

Materials per group: raw egg, 200mL white vinegar, 200mL clear Karo syrup, 200mL water, covered jar, graduated cylinder

Objectives: In this exercise you will:

- Observe osmosis across the membrane of an egg.
- Measure the amount of water that moves across the egg membrane.

In this activity you will be using a raw **(1)**_____ to model a much smaller cell. (A chicken egg is actually a very large **(2)**_____). The egg's shell is made of calcium carbonate, like the shells of marine organisms.

Membranes are beneath the shell. The membranes are **(3)**s_____ p_____, much like the cells of animals. They allow certain substances to pass through. If the shell of a raw egg is removed, the remaining membranes will allow the **(4)**d_____ of substances.

The white part of the egg is albumin. It consists of 15% protein dissolved in **(5)**w_____. The white part of the egg is its **(6)**c_____. The yolk (yellow part) is nutrients for a developing chick embryo (or us).

7-Define:

Cell Membrane

_____

_____

Diffusion

_____

_____

Osmosis

_____

_____

Demonstrating Diffusion & Osmosis: "The Egg Lab"
Always use compete sentences.

8- Day 1 Observations about the egg:

Color _____

Shape _____

Texture (How does it feel?) _____

A. Put 200 ml vinegar in the jar.

B. Place the egg in the jar.

C. Put your FIRST AND LAST NAME on the masking tape on the lid of the jar.

D. Place the jar (and egg & vinegar) in the area labeled for your class.

9- Predict what will happen to the egg sitting in the vinegar overnight.

_____

_____

_____

_____

Demonstrating Diffusion & Osmosis: "The Egg Lab"
USE CARE; DO NOT BREAK EGG.

E. <u>CAREFULLY</u> remove the egg from the vinegar and place it on the jar lid so it won't move.

F. Measure the liquid that is remaining in the jar. Dispose of it in the sink or dump container.

10-How much liquid was remaining in the jar? _____

11-Is that more or less liquid than you put in? _____

12-Day 2 Observations about the egg:

Color _____

Shape _____

Texture (How does it feel?) _____

13- How has the SIZE of the egg changed from the last time you observed it?

_____

_____

14-Did water move into or out of the egg? _____

15-How do you know (two ways)?

_____

_____

16- What happened to the eggshell?

_____

_____

17-Vinegar is made of acetic acid and water. Which part of the vinegar dissolved the shell?

_____

G-Put 200 ml syrup in the jar.
H-Place the egg in the jar.
I-Place the jar (and egg & syrup) in the area labeled for your class.

18-Predict what will happen to the egg sitting in the syrup overnight.

_____

_____

Demonstrating Diffusion & Osmosis: "The Egg Lab"
USE CARE; DO NOT BREAK EGG.

J. **<u>CAREFULLY</u>** remove the egg from the syrup and place it on the jar lid so it won't move.

K. **Measure** the liquid that is remaining in the jar. Dispose of it in the sink or dump container.

19- How much liquid was remaining in the jar? _____

20-Is that more or less liquid than you put in? _____

21-Day 3 Observations about the egg:

Color _____

Shape _____

Texture (How does it feel?) _____

22-How has the SIZE of the egg changed from the last time you observed it?

_____

_____

23-Did water move into or out of the egg? _____

24-How do you know (two ways)?

_____

_____

L. Put 200 ml water in the jar.
M. Place the egg in the jar.
N. Place the jar (and egg & water) in the area labeled for your class.

25-Predict what will happen to the egg sitting in the water overnight.

_____

_____

Demonstrating Diffusion & Osmosis: "The Egg Lab"
USE CARE; DO NOT BREAK EGG.

O. CAREFULLY remove the egg from the water and place it on the jar lid so it won't move.

P. Measure the liquid that is remaining in the jar. Dispose of it in the sink or dump container.

26-How much liquid was remaining in the jar? _____

27-Is that more or less liquid than you put in? _____

28-Day 4 Observations about the egg:

Color _____

Shape _____

Texture (How does it feel?) _____

29-How has the SIZE of the egg changed from the last time you observed it?

_____

_____

30-Did water move into or out of the egg? _____

31-How do you know (two ways)?

_____

_____

32-Do you think the egg was bigger after being in water or after being in vinegar? _____

33-Why?

_____

_____

Analysis:

34-Why would a living cell placed in syrup probably lose water?

_____

_____

35-Why are fresh fruits and vegetables sprinkled with water at the market?

_____

_____

36-Roads are sometimes salted to melt ice. What does this salting do to the plants along the roadside?

_____

_____

37-Why?

_____

_____

38-Why do dried fruits and dried beans swell when they are cooked?

_____

_____

Name_____ Date_____ Period_____ Lab_____

Examining Plant and Animal Cells

MATERIALS: microscope, slides, cover slips, toothpick, iodine stain, methylene blue stain, onion, elodea (water plant)

THE PLANT CELL-White or Yellow Onion

Peel away a very fine layer of tissue from a section of onion. Prepare a wet mount of the tissue of onion. Locate the onion cells under scanning power (4x) of your microscope. Examine the cells under low power (10x) and draw them in pencil below:

1-TRACE THE OUTLINE OF TWO CELLS IN RED.

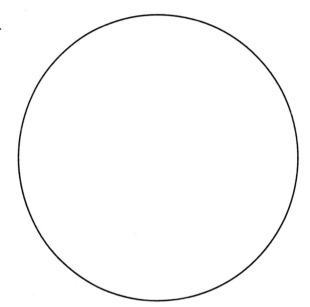

Examine the cells under high power (40x) and draw them in pencil below:

2-Do the cells look bigger or smaller than under low

power? _____

3-Do you see more or less cells? _____

4-TRACE THE OUTLINE OF TWO CELLS IN RED.

5-If you see any nuclei, LABEL each nucleus.

6-Label 3 areas where cytoplasm is located.

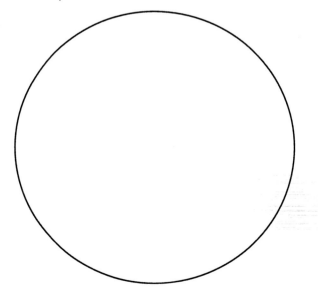

Amber is the color of iodine stain. Add some iodine stain to your onion slide by placing a small piece of paper towel on one side of the cover slip and putting a drop or two of iodine on the other side of the cover slip. The iodine should move under the cover slip and coat the onion tissue. It does this through a process called capillary action. The onion tissue should now look yellow-ish because of iodine's amber color. Use scanning power (4x), then low power (10x) to find the now stained onion cells. Next, locate onion cells under high (40x). Draw them in pencil below. Add yellow for the stain:

7- TRACE THE OUTLINE OF TWO CELL WALLS IN RED.

8- TRACE THE OUTLINE OF TWO MEMBRANES IN BLUE.

(THE CELL WALLS AND MEMBRANES SHOULD BE VERY CLOSE!!)

9-LABEL the cytoplasm in two cells.

10-If you see any nuclei, LABEL each nucleus.

11-What is the purpose of staining cells?

_____

_____

_____

_____

12-What effect do you think stain has on a living cell?

_____

_____

THE PLANT CELL-Elodea Leaf

Obtain an elodea leaf. Prepare a wet mount of the leaf. Locate the plant cells under scanning power (4x) of your microscope. Examine the cells under low power (10x) and draw them in pencil below. Add green color where appropriate:

13-TRACE THE OUTLINE OF TWO CELLS IN RED.

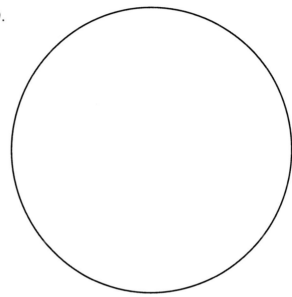

Examine the cells under high power (40x) and draw them in pencil below:

14-Do the cells look bigger or smaller than under low power?

_____

15-Do you see more or less cells? _____

16-TRACE THE OUTLINE OF TWO CELLS IN RED.

17-If you see any nuclei, LABEL each nucleus.

18-Label 2 areas where cytoplasm is located.

19-Label 3 chloroplasts.

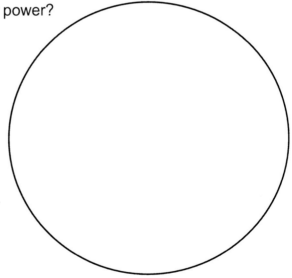

THE ANIMAL CELL

Using the flat end of a toothpick **GENTLY** scrape the inside of your check and tap the scrapings onto the center of a new slide. Prepare a wet mount of your cheek cells. Locate the cheek cells under scanning power (4x) of your microscope. Examine the cells under low power (10x) and draw them in pencil below. (They will appear "ghost-like"):

20-TRACE THE OUTLINE OF TWO CELLS IN RED.

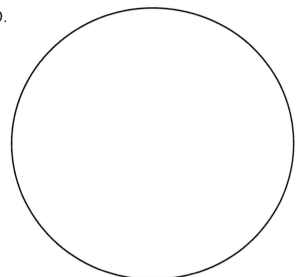

Examine the cells under high power (40x) and draw them in pencil below:

21-Do the cells look bigger or smaller than under low power?

_____

22-TRACE THE OUTLINE OF TWO CELLS IN RED.

23-If you see any nuclei, LABEL each nucleus.

24-Label 2 areas where cytoplasm is located.

25-Cheek cells are animal cells. Compare the shape of these animal cells to the shape of onion plant cells examined previously.

_____

_____

_____

_____

Methylene blue is another kind of stain. Add some methylene blue to your cheek slide by placing a small piece of paper towel on one side of the cover slip and putting a drop or two of methylene blue on the other side of the cover slip. The methylene blue should move under the cover slip and coat the cheek cells. It does this through a process called <u>capillary action</u>. The cheek cells should now look blue. Use scanning power (4x), then low power (10x) to find the now stained cheek cells. Next, locate cheek cells under high (40x). Draw them in pencil below:

26- TRACE THE OUTLINE OF TWO MEMBRANES IN BLUE.

27-LABEL the cytoplasm in two cells.

28-If you see any nuclei, LABEL each nucleus.

29-What is the purpose of staining cells?

_____

_____

_____

_____

30-What effect do you think stain has on a living cell?

_____

DISCARD ALL SLIDES AND COVER SLIPS.

31-List how plant cells are different than animal cells.

PLANT CELLS	ANIMAL CELLS

213

32- When changing from low to high power on a microscope, cells will look b_____.

33- Circle the correct answer: When changing from low to high power on a microscope, you will see (more / fewer) cells.

34- The purpose of staining cells is _____

35- The purpose of a diaphragm on a microscope is _____

36- Plant cells use _____ for photosynthesis. Animal cells don't need them.

37- Plant cells don't use _____ for cell division; that function is carried out by their microtubules.

38- Animal cells don't need a cell _____ for structure.

39- Animal cells use lysosomes to digest worn out cell parts; in plant cells _____ perform this function.

40- Animal cells have small vacuoles called _____.

Name_____ Date_____ Period_____ Lab_____

Understanding Microscopes and Microscopic Measurement

Materials: Microscope, transparent metric ruler

Introduction

Microscopes are useful devices. But like any tool, if used improperly, they will provide little benefit. Learning to correctly use a microscope will allow you to more easily find specimens/cells.

We will begin learning about microscopes by using the letter "e". We all know that an "e" is round with a line connecting the upper half. In this lab, you will use that knowledge to determine how a microscope works.

1- Locate the eyepiece on the microscope. What is the magnifying power of the eye piece?

_____

Notice the scanning objective lens has a magnification of 4x. It is used to view the whole slide (a wider field of vision).

2-The total magnifying power in a microscope is determined by multiplying the magnifying power of the eyepiece by the magnifying power of the objective. What is the total magnifying power using the scanning objective lens?

_____

3-Notice the low-power objective lens has a magnification of 10x. It is used to see the specimen in more detail. What is the total magnifying power using the low-power lens?

_____

4-Notice the high-power objective lens has a magnification of 40x. Though it has a smaller field of vision, it is used to see fine details in a specimen. What is the total magnifying power using the high-power lens?

_____

5- Complete the following MAGNIFICATION CHART:

	Eyepiece Power	Objective Power	Total Magnification
Low Power			
High Power			

FOCUSING THE LETTER "e"

PROCEDURE

A. Lower the stage using the coarse adjustment knob.

B. Place the slide of the letter "e" on the stage. <u>The letter "e" should be facing you like a normal</u>
<u>"e" would look.</u>

C. Center the "e" on the stage.

D. Place the scanning objective lens into position.

E. Looking into the eyepiece, SLOWLY use the coarse adjustment to raise the stage closer to
the objective lens until the object (i.e. "e") comes into focus.

F. Once the object is seen, it may be necessary to adjust the amount of light. To increase or
decrease contrast, rotate the diaphragm slightly.

G. Use the fine adjustment knob to sharpen focus if necessary.

H. Be sure that the "e" is centered in the field of view. If it is not, move the slide with your hands
until you can see the "e" in the center of your scanning field of view.

6-As you look at the "e" at 40x magnification you will notice that magnification makes the "e" look

b_____ than it actually is. You may also notice that the "e" is u_____

d_____ and b_____.

7-Next, put the microscope on LOW POWER. Below- left is what a lower case "e" looks like
before being placed under 100x magnification. Draw what you see in your field of view in the
circle on the lower- right.

e

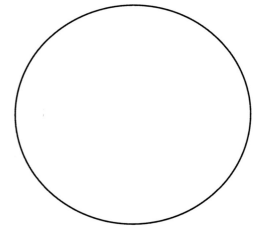

8-Use your hands to move the "e" slide away from you as you're looking at it through the eyepiece. What happens to the microscope image of the "e" when you move the microscope slide away from you?

_____

_____

9-Use your hands to move the "e" slide toward you as you're looking at it through the eyepiece. What happens to the microscope image of the "e" when you move the microscope slide toward you?

_____

_____

10-How do you move the microscope image the right?

_____

_____

11-How do you move the microscope image to the left?

_____

_____

12-Be sure that the image is centered in the field of view and then put the microscope on HIGH power. Use only the fine adjustment knob to focus on high power. Draw and label what you see.

High Power.

13-You should not see the whole letter "e". Explain why not.

_____

_____

Determining FIELD OF VIEW/Microscopic Measurement

PROCEDURE:

A. Lay a transparent ruler across the stage and focus, under low power, on the lines of the metric scale.

B. Position the ruler so that one of the mm lines is just visible at the left of the field of view.

14- Sketch your view in the circle below.

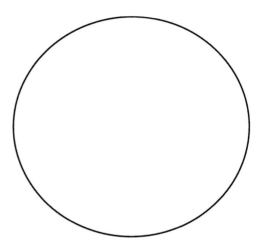

15-The spaces between the lines are all_?_ mm.   _____

16-What is the diameter (distance across) of your low power field of view in mm?

_____

17-1 mm =_?_ µm (micrometers)   _____

18-What is the diameter of your low power field of view in µm?   _____

Viewing the ruler under high power is very difficult because of light and focusing problems. Also, the high-power field of view is smaller than 1 mm, which makes measurements difficult. But you do know several things:

19-Low Power Total Magnification = _____

20-High Power Total Magnification = _____

21-Low Power Field Diameter in µm = _____

22-Calculate the diameter of your high-power field of view in μm using the following formula:

$$\left\{ \frac{\text{Low Power Total Magnification}}{\text{High Power Total Magnification}} \right\} \times \text{Low Power Field Diameter}$$

SHOW ALL YOUR WORK BELOW

23-Complete the following chart in μm:

Field	Diameter in μm
Low Power	
High Power	

Cut out a "-" and make a wet mount of the "-". Focus it under low power.

24-What is the length of the "-" in μm?   _____

25-What is the width if the "-" in μm?   _____

26-Sketch the view of the"-" in the circle below.

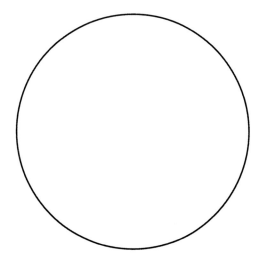

PRACTICE

The field of view has an image of a unicellular organism. The field of view is under low power.

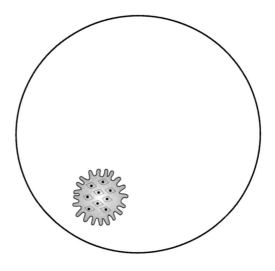

27-What is the length of the single celled organism in µm?   _____

The field of view has an image of a Paramecium. It is viewed under high power.

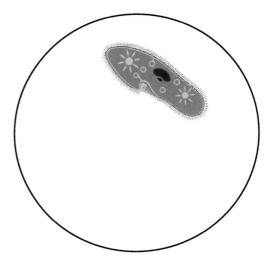

28-What is the length of the paramecium in µm?   _____

29-What is the width of the paramecium in µm?   _____

Lab Manual Answer Key

Biochemistry

Identifying Organic Compounds

1-light blue

2-brick red

3-glucose

4-amber

5-blue/black

6-starch

7-an unchanged variable

8-used to compare to manipulated variable

9-oil

10-lipid

11-light purple

12-pink/purple/fuchsia

13-protein

14-glucose

15-starch

16-lipid

17-protein

Investigating pH

pH Investigation Table- typical household acids and bases, pH may differ

lemon juice	glass cleaner	soda	bottled water	rainwater	orange juice	bleach
acid	base	acid	neutral range	acid	acid	base

1-potential/percent of hydrogen

2-lemon juice, soda, rainwater, orange juice

3-glass cleaner, bleach

4-possibly bottled water

Effect of low pH on organic compound table: Distilled water will keep the pH of milk closer to neutral and will simply make the milk waterier. Vinegar will lower the pH of milk and cause it to curdle.

5-Will the pH of milk change the pH and composition of milk?

6-milk and distilled water

7-milk and vinegar

8-The pH of milk became more acidic/decreased and the milk curdled.

9-The pH of water varies according to the source.

10-more acidic; 100x

11-a base.

12-Living things have enzymes and proteins which function best at certain pH's.

13-answer should show a fully labeled pH scale with the substances tested at the correct points on the scale.

Molecular Modeling

1-a compound that has carbon bonded to hydrogen

2-carbohydrates, fats, proteins

3-carbon, hydrogen, oxygen

4-nitrogen

5-a bond where atoms share electrons

6-H:1, C:4, O:2, N:3

7-

$$H-\underset{\underset{H}{|}}{\overset{\overset{H}{|}}{C}}-\underset{\underset{H}{|}}{\overset{\overset{H}{|}}{C}}-H$$

8-Oxygen

9-Water

10-Carbon Dioxide; Students build organic models for instructor to check

11-Fats, carbohydrates, and proteins are considered organic because they contain carbon bonded to hydrogen. The molecules oxygen, water, and carbon dioxide don't contain both of those elements and, therefore, are not organic.

Observing the Enzyme Catalase

1-denatured

2-Labeled pH scale should be drawn in this space

3-Labeled lock and key model should be drawn in this space

4-changed

5-bubbling

6-oxygen

7-warmer

8-exothermic

Table 1: 3-4

9-water

10-yes

11-yes

Table 2:

	0-4	Re-lights	Y/N
Test 1	3-4	varies	Y
Test 2	0	0	N
Test 3	0	0	N
Test 4	4	varies	Y
Test 5	0	0	N
Test 6	0	0	N

12-proteins that speed up reactions

13-room temperature and pulverized liver

14-acidic, alkaline/basic, boiled, and frozen liver

15-caused the shape to change

16-The substrate reacts with a larger amount of the enzyme. It provides the most surface area.

Cellular Energy

Cellular Respiration in Plants

Data Table- Answers vary, but color change in Bromthymol blue for germinating seeds should take about 45 minutes.

1-it changes from blue to green to yellow.

2-decreases

3-the non-germinating seeds were the control.

4-the color change in the BTB

5-cotton allows air/gasses to move through

6-The concentration of oxygen will decrease in the test tube with germinating seeds.

7-Oxygen diffuses into root cells; Carbon dioxide diffuses out of root cells.

8-Respiration rate would decrease with no fresh oxygen.

9-Animal cells may have more mitochondria, which would increase the respiration rate in animal cells versus plant cells.

10-Carbon dioxide

11-cellular/aerobic respiration

12-photosynthesis

13-oxygen

14-carbon dioxide

Chromatography

1-bands

2A-its attraction to the absorbent (paper)

2B-its ability to dissolve (solubility) in solvent (water)

3-move slowly and be left behind

4-move quickly and accumulate near the first water molecules that pass along the paper

5-water

6-seperating small quantities of substances which occur in mixtures

7-prevents contamination of samples

8-Chlorophylll covers up other pigments.

9-Answers vary- those with most similar chromatograms.

10-Answers vary-those with least similar chromatograms.

11-Those most closely related will use similar pigments to perform photosynthesis and, thus, have more similar bands.

12a-Answers vary

12b-Answers vary

Fermentation in Yeast

1-Carbon dioxide

2-Carbon dioxide, yellow/green/answers vary

3-food

4-sugar is a simple carbohydrate

5-Increasing temperature, to a point, increases fermentation.

6-If done correctly, yes.

7-Carbon dioxide is present. BTB might not be dilute enough/There was not enough carbon dioxide leaving the yeast/The container was not air-tight.

8-Aerobic means with air/oxygen; Anaerobic means without air/oxygen

9-Lactic Acid

10-Lactic acid is produced during rapid exercise when the body can't supply enough oxygen to produce ATP . Muscle cells produce ATP through lactic acid fermentation.

Observing Photosynthesis

1-Water, sunlight, carbon dioxide

2-The process of using water, sunlight, and carbon dioxide to make food.

3-chlorophyll

4-Chlorophyll is green. Chlorophyll reflects green light, so we see it.

5-ATP

6-Sugar and organic compounds

7-It can happen at night; there is no light needed

8-To see how plants exchange gases (oxygen/carbon dioxide) during photosynthesis.

9-blueish

10-Blowing through a straw

11-green/yellow

12-Carbon dioxide

13-Green

14-Carbon dioxide

15-blue-ish

16-Diagram should show oxygen leaving plant and going to animal; diagram should show carbon dioxide leaving animal and going to plant. Sentences should explain the CO_2/O_2 cycle.

Classification

Classifying Animals

1-Binomial nomenclature

2-The genus name is capitalized; the species name is not

3-Scientists previously uses shared traits of organisms to determine common ancestry. Now traits are observed in combination with genetics.

4-Kingdom, Phylum, Class, Order, Family, Genus, Species

5-Animalia, Chordata, Mammalia, Primata, Hominidae, Homo

6-Answers vary. Groupings of like cards should have logical descriptions of commonalities.

7-Answers vary.

8-Answers vary. Possible responses include that biologists may have made microscopic observations or done DNA or RNA or Amino Acid analysis.

Classifying Animal Cards		
GROUP	WHICH ANIMALS ARE IN THIS GROUP? (NUMBERS)	WHAT DO THE ANIMALS IN EACH GROUP HAVE IN COMMON?
Platyhelminthes	2, 5, 19	• Flat worm • Gases move through skin through diffusion • Soft body
Cnidaria	3, 7, 20	• Tentacles/stinging cells • Water moves through body • Oxygen/food flow with water though tissues
Annelida	4, 9, 12	• Segmented • Oxygen moves through skin/diffusion • Needs water/moisture
Mollusca	10, 14, 17	• Soft body • Uses foot to move
Arthropoda	8, 11, 15	• Exoskeleton • Jointed legs
Chordata	6, 13, 16	• Vertebrae • Complex nervous and circulatory system
Echioderm	1, 18, 21	• Radial symmetry • Marine dwelling • Three germ layers

Dichotomous Keys

1-Possible answers: number of fins, body shape, mouth placement, presence/absence of spine, etc.

2-
A-*Rhincondon typus*	Whale Shark
B-*Carcharadon carcharias*	Great White Shark
C-*Iteterodontus francisci*	Horn Shark
D-*Somniosus microcephalus*	Greenland Shark
E-*Sphyrna zygaena*	Smooth hammerhead
F-*Squatina squatina*	Angel Shark

3-Answers vary.

4-Possible answers: smell, color, size of organisms, etc.

5-A dichotomous key is a tool that is used to sort and identify organisms. It is not based on evolutionary relationships. A cladogram organisms into categories that reflect evolutionary descent.

Silly Science Classification

A-whatnot

B-flipsey

C-screecher

D-gadget

E-dipsey

F-fancy whatnot

G-itsy-bitsy

H-oopsey

I-cubey

J-super duper

K-squealer

L-fuzzy

M-gumby

N-mipsey

Understanding Taxonomy

1-Domain, kingdom

2-species

3-Linnaeus and Woese

4-Eukaryotic organisms have cells with nuclei; prokaryotic organisms have cells without nuclei

5-they have nuclei in their cells

6-genus and species

7-Species is written starting with a lower-case letter; Genus is written starting with an upper-case letter. Both are italicized.

8-all are animals

9-flying

10-true

11-The taxons are "nested". The bigger taxons include the smaller taxons.

12-Possible answers include donkey, camel, giraffe, hippopotamus, etc.

13-_Balaenoptera musculus, Pan troglodyte, Musca domestica_

14-_B. musculus, P. troglodyte, M. domestica_

15-Answers vary

16-Answers vary

Extra Credit-Answers vary

Ecology

Adapted for Survival? Bird Adaptations to Habitat

A successfully completed lab will have:

- An accurately drawn and colored habitat
- Seven sentences about the student's bird species that follow the conventions outlined in the lab
- Circles around the student's chosen beak type, foot type, and nest type
- An accurately drawn and colored bird and nest which reflects the beak, foot, and nest circled.

1-9-Answers vary.

8 and 9 should reference the species' ability to reproduce and pass its genetic material on to its offspring.

10-survive, reproduce, offspring, Selection

Calculating Exponential Growth

1-Year 1: 6 (3 pairs/couples)

Year 2: 3 couples produce 6 each

(3 x 6 = 18 or 9 couples)

Year 3: 9 couples produce 6 each

(9 x 6 = 54 or 27 couples)

Year 4: 27 couples produce 6 each

(27 x 6 = 162 or 81 couples)

Year 5: 81 couples produce 6 each

(81 x 6 = 486 or 243 couples)

2-Exponential Growth

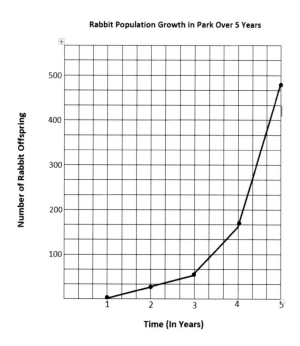

3-118,098 (approximately 120,000), 6,973,568,802 (approximately 7 billion)

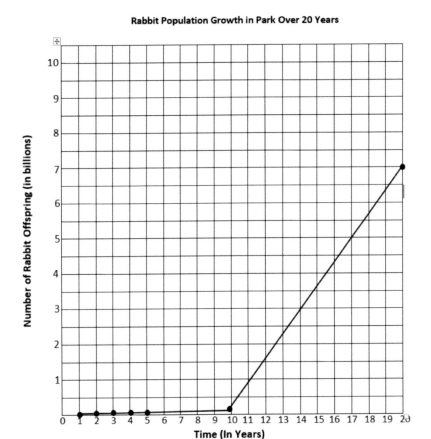

Rabbit Population Growth in Park Over 20 Years

A)The population would decline due to starvation, disease, parasitism, predation, etc.

B)Natural predators, disease, limited supply of resources such as food, water, shelter, and mates limit the population. Not all offspring survive to maturity. Some adults don't reproduce.

Predator-Prey Relationships

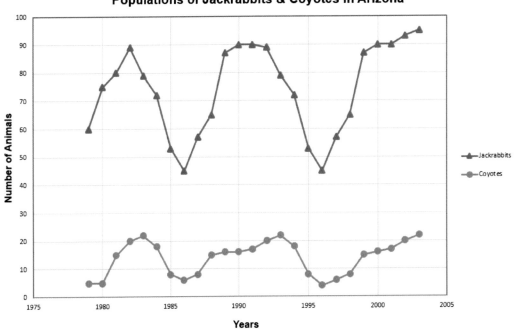

Populations of Jackrabbits & Coyotes in Arizona

1-Answers vary. Both the jackrabbits and coyote data lines mirror each other, with three upward and two downward trends.

2-Cyclic graphs show repeating trends, as does this one.

Studying Population Growth

1-Phase when organisms are adjusting to the new environment and the population shows little increase in numbers.

2-Phase where the birth rate is greater than the death rate. Occurs when nutrients are available, and the environment is favorable to the organisms.

3-Phase where the birth rate equals the death rate; the population is constant.

4-Phase where the death rate is greater than the birth rate.

5-Exhaustion of food supplies or accumulation of wastes.

Growth of Bacterial Population	
Time (hr)	Number of Organisms
0	1500
1	2000
2	4000
3	7000
4	14,000
5	30,000
6	59,000
7	71,000
8	76,000
9	77,000
10	74,000
11	67,000
12	58,000
13	45,000
14	35,000

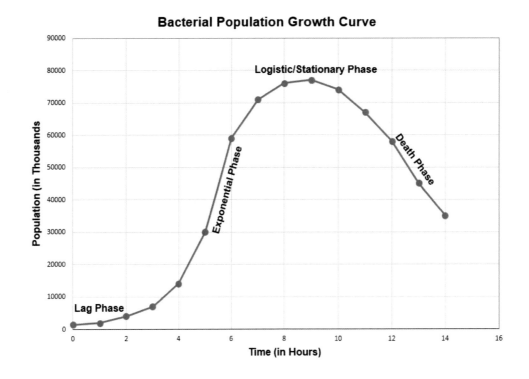

Bacterial Population Growth Curve

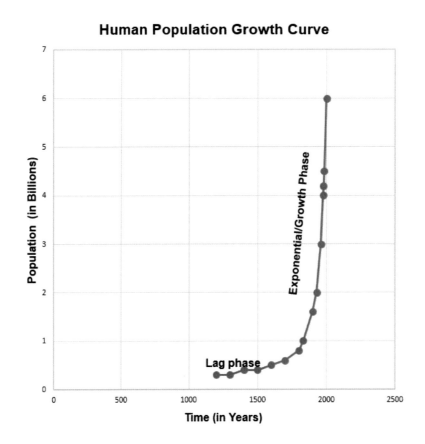

Human Population Growth Curve

6- 230 years
7- 45 years
8- Exponential/Growth

Evolution

Antibiotic Resistance

1-Answers vary.

Table 1-Answers vary. Pebbles should increase very quickly.

Graph 1-Answers vary. Graph should show pebbles increasing. There should be a title, appropriate scales and a key. The x-axis is number of bacteria; the y-axis is dose and reproduction.

2-80%

3-9

4-Answers vary. With larger numbers, bacteria would take longer to develop resistance. Small numbers were used in this activity for demonstration purposes.

5-Normal.

6-Toothpick = hand sanitizer.

Table 2-

Traits	Normal Bacteria-Description: cylindrical, soft-bodied, beige	Mutated Bacteria-Description: irregular shape, hard-bodied, tan, brown, black, grey, white
Adaptive Advantage (Traits That Helped Survival)	None	Hard-bodied
Unfavorable Traits	Soft-bodied	None
Unaffected Traits	Cylindrical, beige	Irregular shape, tan, brown, black, grey, white

7-Hard-bodied. Toothpick couldn't "get" bacteria.

8-Soft-bodied. Toothpick could "get" bacteria.

9-Bacteria not killed will reproduce and pass on their genes that helped them survive. Over time, the population of bacteria will have large numbers of resistant bacteria.

10-Organisms with favorable traits survive and reproduce. Over time, the population evolves so most of the organisms have the favorable trait—like antibiotic resistance.

11-Answers vary. Prescribing an antibiotic for someone who may not have a bacterial infection still results in killing bacteria in the body. If these helpful bacteria die off it will provide an opportunity for harmful, resistant bacteria to flourish.

12-Answers vary. Antibiotic resistant bacteria result from natural selection—as do insecticide resistant insects. Both are becoming more common . Knowledge of this can help us make smart decisions about how to better control bacteria and insects.

Describing the Elements of Evolution

1-
- Many more snakes are born than can survive
- Among those snakes, there are many differences/variations
- Those snakes with rotating mandibles are more fit because they are able to get better nutrition
- This larger mouth opening would have made them more fit for their environment
- Over time, snakes with rotating mandibles would pass their genes to their offspring, so the population of snakes would be better adapted to the environment.

2-
- Many more orchids are produced than can survive
- Among those orchids, there are many variations
- The orchids with pseudocopulatory parts are more fit because they will be cross-pollinated by insects
- The special structures make the orchids in the environment
- Over time, orchids with pseudocopulatory structures will be found more in the population because those genes that are best adapted will be passed on to offspring.

3-
- Many more bacteria are produced than can survive
- All bacteria have natural differences
- The bacteria that are naturally resistant to antibiotics will be most fit in the environment.
- When antibiotics are applied, only those naturally resistant will survive.
- As a result of their survival, they will be able to pass their genes onto their offspring, and, over time the species will be better adapted to an environment with antibiotics.

4-
- Many more deer mice are born than can survive
- There are natural differences among the mice
- Only those mice with paler coat color will survive in Nebraska
- The pale colored mice will live in Nebraska because predators won't see them
- As a result, the pale colored mice will be able to reproduce and pass their genes to their offspring.

5-
- Many more diamond back moths are born than can survive.
- There are differences among the moths.
- Those moths that are naturally insecticide resistant are more fit.
- When insecticide is applied, insecticide resistant moths will live.
- Those moths will then be able to reproduce and pass their genes on to their offspring, eventually making the moth population better adapted to their environment.

6-
- On both islands, many more caltrops are produced than can survive
- There are natural variations in the caltrop plant.

- Depending on the island, tough coats or numerous seeds, will have a selective advantage.
- Depending on the island (whether the *G. fortis* bird is present), tough coats or numerous seed plants will survive .
- On the island with the birds, the tougher seed plants will survive and pass their genes to their offspring; on the island without the birds, the numerous seed plants will survive and pass their genes to their offspring. Over time, the plant species on the respective islands will become better adapted.

7-Answers vary.

Patterns of Natural Selection

1-The extremes at both ends disappear and the population stays relatively stable.

2-It gets rid of one end of the scale; the average trait becomes greater/lesser than before.

3-It gets rid of the "normal"/average organisms. Only the extremes survive. Often leads to a new species forming.

4-b

5-c

6-a

7-c

8-b

9-The extremes. For example, the longest and shortest.

10-Directional selection

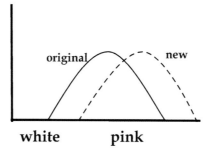

white   pink

11a-Disruptive

11b-Directional

11c-Stabilizing

12-Curve should be drawn showing a shift toward larger seeds.

13-Birds with large/thick beaks

14-If there were fewer small seeds there would not be enough food for the birds with the small beaks. They may die before they reproduce. The birds with big beaks would have enough food and live long enough to reproduce and pass their genes on to their offspring.

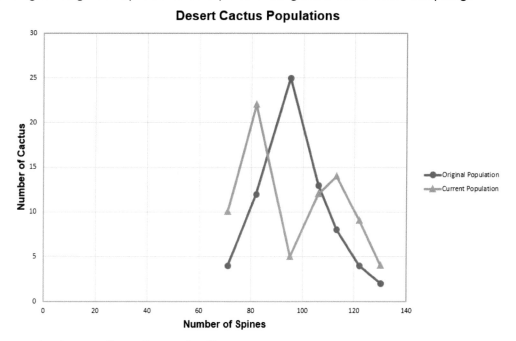

Desert Cactus Populations

15- This graph shows disruptive selection.

Where Do Pandas Fit in the Tree of Life?

1-One scientist thought the giant panda looked like a bear of the outside; another scientist did an autopsy/postmortem and thought the giant panda was related to racoons.

2-The upward curve on the lower jaw is very large in the giant panda and somewhat large in the red panda. The tops of the giant and red panda skulls are more angled.

3-There are larger grinding/surface areas on the teeth of the red and giant pandas.

4-The fake thumb is larger in the red and giant pandas.

5-Answers vary. Yes. The great panda moves like bears. They also have a similar appearance, similar skeleton, muscles, and organs including lungs and brain.

6-Bamboo

7-Mostly bamboo and other plants, fruit, and insects

8-Extra-large molars and over-grown jaw muscles

9-bear, tough plants

10-wrists, thumb

11-Several other animals in the carnivore family have large radial sesamoid bones, especially those that climb trees.

12-Brown bears and giant pandas had the most similar DNA sequences.

13-Giant pandas had only one less pair of chromosomes than red pandas and only two more than racoons.

14-The giant panda's chromosomes are bigger than the brown bear's and the giant panda's centromere is in the center, not at the end.

15-banding pattern

16-hemoglobin

17-

Which Lineage Are Giant Pandas Most Similar To? B = Bears / R = Red Pandas & Racoons / Mixed	
Evidence:	B or R or M?
Anatomy-Skull	R/M
Anatomy-Teeth	R/M
Anatomy-Front Paw/Pseudothumb	R/M
Anatomy-Body Size	B
Anatomy-Skeleton	B
Anatomy-Muscles	B
Anatomy-Internal Organs	B
Behavior-Diet	R/M
Fossils	M
Biochemistry-DNA Hybridization	B
Biochemistry-Number of Chromosomes	R
Biochemistry-Chromosome Banding Patterns	B
Biochemistry-Hemoglobin Amino Acid Sequences	R

18-Answers vary.

Genetics

Animal Body Plans

1-Symmetry, number of body segments, number of limbs

2-They are responsible for laying down the basic body plan of organisms.

3-Allows for specialization (stomach, intestines, etc.)

4-Ectoderm (outside), Mesoderm (middles), Endoderm (inside)

5-The first organism is asymmetrical, no line of symmetry can be drawn

Bilateral Symmetry

6-Specialization (e.g. antennae, eyes, claws, legs, etc.)

7-They are master switches that turn on and off arrays of other genes involved in body shape and controlling number, pattern, position, and fusion of segments and appendages.

8-They are master switches determining cell fates, growth, and development.

9-40

10-They have similar homeobox gene sequences.

11-The same hox genes determine both.

12-The same hox gene switches on eye formation in all animals with eyes.

DNA Fingerprint

1-The victim scratched themselves; they scratched another person; evidence tampering/planted evidence

2-DNA is unique to each person, like fingerprints.

3-an enzyme that recognized a bond with a specific short base sequence of DNA

4-cuts DNA samples at specific sites within the sequence

5-seperates the DNA when electric current is applied to the gel

6-DNA has a negative charge

7-Smaller fragments travel farther than larger fragments.

8-banding pattern, fragments

9-No

10-The DNA of the skin under the victim's fingernails doesn't match the victim's DNA.

11-3

12-The victim scratched the suspect (3), perhaps during a struggle to the death.

13-Answers vary. DNA is unique to each individual, so if there is DNA under the victim's fingernails this is not his own, there needs to be an explanation.

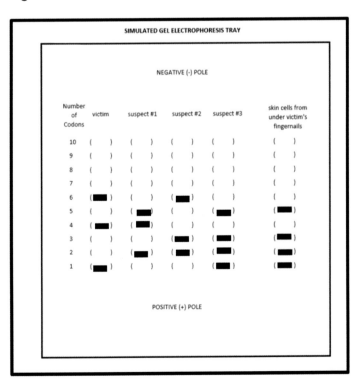

Protein Synthesis

1-GCTAACCGTCAGTATCCGATTCTA

2-	ALA	ASN	ARG	GLN	TYR	PRO	ILE	LEU
	GCU	AAC	CGU	CAG	UAU	CCG	AUU	CUA
	white	green	orange	pink	white	brown	lt blue	dk blue
3-	ALA	TYR	ARG	GLN	TYR	PRO	ILE	LEU
	GCU	UAC	CGU	CAG	UAU	CCG	AUU	CUA
	white	white	orange	pink	white	brown	lt blue	dk blue
4-	ALA	GLN	PRO	SER	VAL	SER	ASP	SER
	GCU	CAA	CCG	UCA	GUA	UCC	GAU	UCU
	white	pink	brown	red	black	red	yellow	red

A

5-Number 3 was a substitution mutation. There was one difference in the amino acid chain: TYR/white instead of ASN/green. This represents a point mutation. Number 4 was an addition/insertion mutation. There were seven differences in the amino acid chain. Every amino acid was different after the first one. This represents a frame shift mutation.

Normal Protein (#2) Colors: white, green, pink, white, brown, lt blue, dk blue- no mutation

Mutated Protein (#3) Colors: white, white, orange, pink, white, brown, lt blue, dk blue- substitution mutation

Mutated Protein (#4) Colors: white, pink, brown, red, black, red, yellow, red- addition/insertion mutation

Variations Within A Population

Data Table 1-Answers vary. Typical range 20-50 mm.

Data Table 2-Answers vary. Most peanut shells will be 30-40 mm.

Lengths of Peanut Shells Graph-Answers vary. Bell shaped graph is typical.

Data Table 3-Answers vary.

Data Table 4-Answers vary. Typical handspan range is 15-30 cm.

Handspans of Students Graph-Answers vary. Bell shaped graph is typical.

A-Differences---in this case, among species.

B and C-Answers vary.

D-Bell shape/normal curve

E and F-Answers vary.

G-Bell shape/normal curve

H-Provides protection for more sees so that the plant is able to have more offspring

I-Answers vary. Hold tools better; defense against enemies/predators

J-The plant would be able to produce more offspring.

K-It's ability to get water would be limited.

L-It would provide better camouflage so it could hide from its predators and surprise its prey.

Human Body Systems

Digestive System

Students are to cut the different colored yarns to the requisite lengths, according to their body proportions.

To measure the small intestine, they need to show the calculation of their height in centimeters times four.

They are to list their height in centimeters and meters.

Digestive System Data Table-Answers vary.

Approximate length of the digestive tract in meters-the average adult digestive tract is 8 meters long.

1-Answers vary. The digestive system is greater than an individual's height. The digestive system is 4-5 times greater than the height of the individual.

2-There are many folds.

3-There needs to be more area for greater nutrient absorption.

4-small intestine

5-Increased surface area allows for increased absorption of nutrients.

6-D	16-B
7-F	17-N
8-N, H	18-L
9-O	19-M
10-J	20-A
11-C	21-K
12-H	22-M
13-I	23-G
14-M	24-M
15-E	

Structure of the Kidney and Nephron

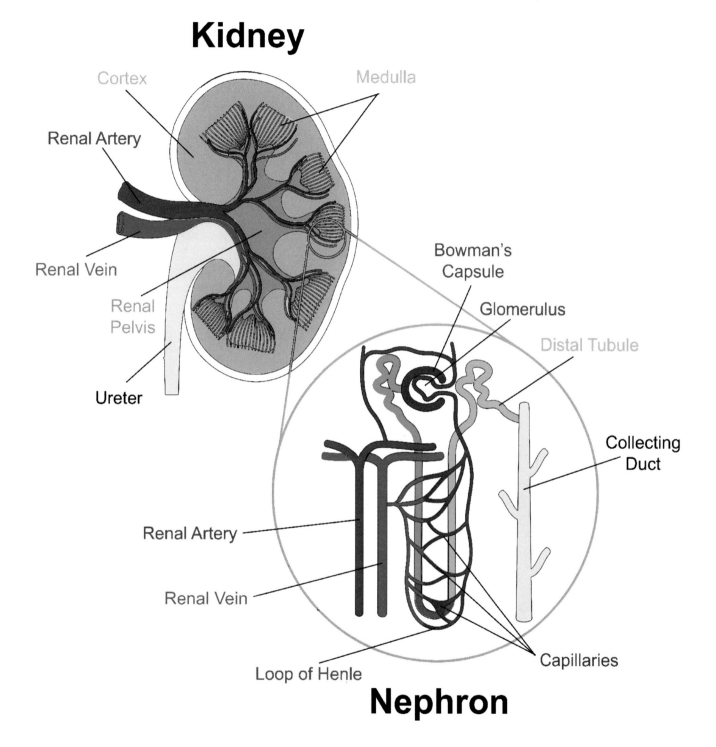

Kidney

Cortex

Medulla

Renal Artery

Renal Vein

Renal Pelvis

Ureter

Bowman's Capsule

Glomerulus

Distal Tubule

Collecting Duct

Renal Artery

Renal Vein

Capillaries

Loop of Henle

Nephron

1-The basic functional unit of the kidney.

2-Glomerulous-filtration of blood. Water and dissolved particles pulled out of the blood.

Bowman's Capsule-contains the glomerulus; filtrate is collected in Bowman's Capsule for transport through the nephron.

Tubule-further concentration and water removal of filtrate. Preparation for transport of urine out of body.

3-Blood to renal artery to glomerulus (in Bowman's Capsule) to nephron to proximal tubule to Loop of Henley to distal tubule to collecting duct/renal pelvis to ureter to bladder.

4-One million

5-nutrients, water, waste

6-It enters the ureter and then moves to the bladder

7-Two

8-

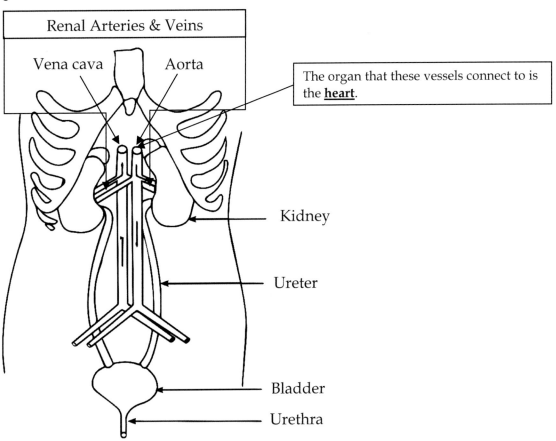

Nervous System

Students need to color code the neuron according to directions on front of lab.

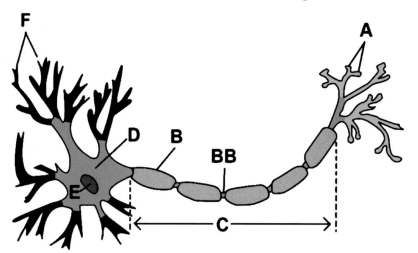

A Axon Terminals

B Myelin Sheath

BB Node of Ranvier

C Axon

D Soma / Cell Body

E Nucleus

F Dendrites

1-The neurotransmitter diffuses into the synaptic cleft and binds to receptors on the membrane (dendrites) of the post synaptic cell. (The shape must fit).

2-4

3-Dendrites are at "A"

4-4

5-3

6-4

7-Answers vary. Cut in nerve cell; Failure to release chemical transmitter; Lack of food/oxygen; The cells are weak; The stimulus was weak; The nerve cell is dead.

8a-coordination and balance

8b-vital body functions; breathing rate; heart rate

8c-sensory and motor integration

8d-body temperature, emotions, hunger, thirst, appetite, sleep, digestion

8e-allows communication between the two brain hemispheres

8f-motor control and sensory analysis

8g-part of CNS; coordinates brain and the rest of the body; walking; reflexes

8h-thinking, voluntary movement, language, reasoning, judgement

8i-controls hormones and helps turn food into energy

j-   k-

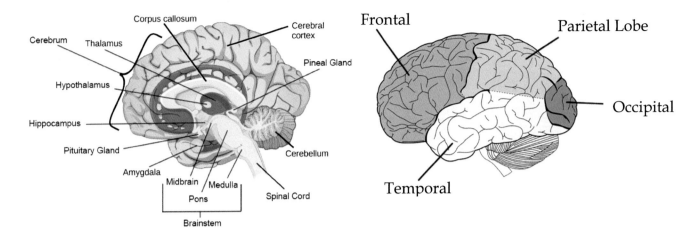

l-frontal, occipital, temporal, parietal

Understanding Viruses

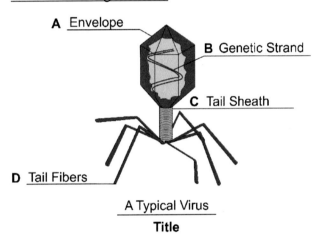

A Typical Virus
Title

1-shape

2-nonliving particle

3-crystal, tissue

4-genetic strand

5-tail sheath/fibers

6-land on a cell

7-Its tail fibers allow it to only land on bacteria or archaea cells.

8-

Virus

Receptor (Envelope) Proteins

Genetic Material/ Viral Genome

Capsid/Envelope

9-Drifts along/transmitted by chance: sneeze, cough, handshake, kiss, hug, dirty dishes, animal bite, sex, hypodermic needles.

10-Viruses have receptor proteins that look like something the cell needs, e.g. nutrients.

11-When a virus gets into the cell.

12-The viruses genetic material reprograms the host cell's nucleus to send instructions for making new viruses.

13-   Step 1: Proteins on the virus bind to receptors on the cell membrane.

   Step 2: Once inside the cell, the virus puts its DNA/RNA into the cell.

   Step 3: The virus' DNA/RNA tells the cell to build more copies of the virus.

   Step 4: New viruses are released through budding or destroying the host cell.

Reproduction

Diagramming Embryological Development

1-conception

2-zygote

3-cleavage

4-morula

5-grow

6-placenta and amniotic sac

7-carries oxygen and nutrients from mother to embryo and waste from embryo to mother

8-space for new life to grow

9-Gastrulization is the formation of specialized cells that are differentiated, not pluripotent.

10-hormones

11-Amniotic sac contains fluid. There must be water, so eggs don't dry out.

12-ectoderm, endoderm, mesoderm

13-skin, nervous system; muscle, skeletal system; digestive, respiratory system

14-embryo, fetus

15-mitosis, sex cells/gametes/sperm and eggs

16-6

17-Fertilization and Implantation diagram:

18-Germ layers are mesoderm, endoderm, and ectoderm

19-Pluripotent can become any kind of cell; they are stem cells. Differentiated cells are specialized to do different jobs.

Diagramming Meiosis

1-Somatic cells are body cells. Sex cells are gametes: sperm or eggs.

2-to produce daughter cells that are genetically identical to their mother/parent cells.

3-to make daughter cells with half as many chromosomes as the starting/parent cell.

4-diploid, haploid

5-sex, gamete

6-46, 23

7-The cell goes through similar stages and uses similar strategies to organize and separate chromosomes.

8-chromatids, homologous

9-identical

10-crossing-over

11-The similar, but non-identical chromosome pairs an organism receives from its two parents.

12-The somatic number: two sets of chromosomes, one from each parent

13-A cell with a single set of chromosomes

14-4, haploid

15-Homologoes pairs randomly orient; crossing-over—homologues exchange genetic material

16-Not all gametes would have the "n" number of chromosomes. This is called non-disjunction.

Meiosis Table

Picture	Phase	Key Points – What Happens
	Interphase	DNA Replication forming duplicate chromosomes
	Prophase I	Homologous (paired) chromosomes form tetrads
	Metaphase I	Spindle fibers attach to the chromosomes
	Anaphase I	Fibers pull chromosomes to opposite ends of the cell
	Telophase I	Nuclear membranes form
	Cytokinesis	The cell separates into two cells
	Prophase II	Each of the two daughter cells has ½ the number of chromosomes as original cell
	Metaphase II	Chromosomes line up similar to metaphase in mitosis
	Anaphase II	Sister chromatids separate and move toward opposite ends of the cell
	Telophase II	Nuclear membranes form
	Cytokinesis	Meiosis results in 4 haploid daughter cells

Observing the Cell Cycle in Onion Root Tips

1-Cells increase in mass and replicate DNA.

2-Cells might not grow and/or might not replicate DNA.

3-The nucleus/chromosomes/DNA/genetic material wouldn't divide correctly.

4-Interphase; Cells spend 90-95% of their time in interphase.

5-Blood cells of bone marrow, skin cells, cells lining the stomach and intestines.

6-The body needs a regular supply of new/fresh blood; The stomach and intestinal cells need to be refreshed regularly due to digestion.

7-Interphase, chromatin, nucleolus

8-Prophase   9-Prophase   10-Metaphase, chromosomes

11-Anaphase   12-Cell Plate   13-Interphase   14-Mitosis

Identify, Order, & Describe Cell Cycle Stages

Stage	Diagram	Photograph	Description of what's happening in each stage
Interphase			Nuclear membrane intact; Chromatin is seen inside nucleus
Prophase			Nuclear membrane is breaking down; Chromosomes are seen inside nucleus
Metaphase			Chromosomes meet in the middle of the cell and are attached to the spindle
Anaphase			Sister chromatids are pulling apart and moving toward the poles
Telophase			Cell plate/wall is beginning to form
Cytokinesis → Draw how this would look. (Attach additional paper, if necessary).			There are now two daughter cells

What Limits the Sizes of Cells?

A and B-Answers vary.

1-Typically the egg cube will be completely blue/dark, and the blue food coloring will penetrate the whole egg about .5 cm.

2-Volume increases faster than surface area. The cell membrane can't deal with the large amount of nutrients that would need to enter the cell, nor the large quantity of wastes that would need to leave the cell.

3-Answers vary. The ratio of surface area to volume should be smaller for the whole egg than for the cube; Small objects have a large ratio of surface area to volume (SA › Vol), large objects have a small ratio of surface area to volume (SA ‹ Vol).

4-4 x 4 x 6 = 96 cm^2 = SA; 4 x 4 x 4 = 64 cm^2 = Vol; 96/64 = 3/2 = 3 : 2 SA/Vol

5-Answers vary. Possible answers: A mitochondrion might not be able to get enough oxygen from outside the cell in order to perform cellular respiration; A chloroplast might not be able to get enough water from outside the cell in order to perform photosynthesis.

Scientific Inquiry

Metric Measurement

Chart 1-meter, gram, liter

Chart 2-meter, gram, liter; ruler, balance, graduated cylinder

1-The metric system is base ten

Chart 3-Answers vary.

2-The penny is smaller so a smaller unit should be used than for a long piece of yarn.

Chart 4-Answers vary.

Chart 5-Answers vary/teacher sign off.

3-Graduated cylinders have more measurement lines.

4-It is the "curve" at the top of liquid in a narrow container.

5-The water in liquids is attracted to other objects. If the sides of the meniscus is read rather than the bottom of the curve, the measurement will be inaccurate.

6-left

7-large, small

8-Human error, evaporation, erosion, different measurement tool.

9A-M

9B-g/mg

9C-cm

9D-Kl

9E-KM

9F-M

9G-mg

Scientific Design: Ethics and Experimenter Bias

1-Prisoners can't exercise free will/Can't say "no" to testing.

2-Leaving an open wound on a person harms them. Introducing objects allow bacteria to enter. This harms the research subject.

3-Research subjects were harmed without their knowledge.

4-Unrepresentative sample & too small of a sample. Smokers are more likely to be in an area where smoking is allowed; the rate of smoking will appear higher than it actually is. Thirty students out of a student body of an unknown number.

5-Non-random sample: 75 of the students were principal selected. The principal would tend to select non-smokers so the rate of student smokers would appear lower than it really is.

6-A) No Butts believe children/teenagers shouldn't be exposed to cigarette ads. B) All of their messages will be anti-smoking/smoking advertising. C) Newboro Cigarette Company believes advertising doesn't encourage children/teens to smoke. They want to sell cigarettes. D) They are motivated to have teen smoking numbers look low.

Scientific Experimentation: Grasshoppers and Heart Medicine

1-Larger grasshoppers jump 3 times farther than smaller grasshoppers.	11-3
2A-lined paper	12-2
2B-checkered shirt	13-Yes. 91% is efficacious.
3A-checkered shirt used to judge distance	14-No. 58% is not much better than placebo.
3B-lined paper used to judge size	15-educated guess
4-10 big grasshoppers jumped 128 checks; 10 small grasshoppers jumped 57 checks.	16-results are outcomes; conclusion is opinion
5-The larger grasshoppers jumped farther than the small grasshoppers.	17-an unchanged variable
6-Larger grasshoppers jumped twice as far as the smaller grasshoppers.	18-base of comparison
7-The boys went back to camp and told the others.	19-something that changes
8-The entire group repeated the experiment and got the same result.	20-The results will be ambiguous if there are too many variables.
9-1	21-A harmless substance
10-2 and 3	22-The mind can "trick" itself with positive thinking/mind over matter

Understanding Scientific Inquiry with Butterfly Puddling

Hypothesis

1-gathering around a moist or watery area

2-butterflies are doing population control; butterflies are consuming nitrogen/amino acids; butterflies are consuming sodium

3-A basis of comparison

4-trays of sand and sodium chloride, trays of sand and amino acids, trays of sand and sugar solution

5-trays of sand and distilled water, trays of sand

6-using senses to determine something (sight, hear, smell, touch, taste)

7-sampling occurs in less than 15 seconds; puddling occurs in 15 seconds or longer

8-Researchers need to determine if butterflies are attracted to the tray or the environment in which tray is located.

9-This avoids researcher bias.

10-The number of puddling visits compared to sampling visits in trays 1, 2, and 3 decreased.

11-The number of puddling visits compared to sampling visits in trays 4 and 5 increased.

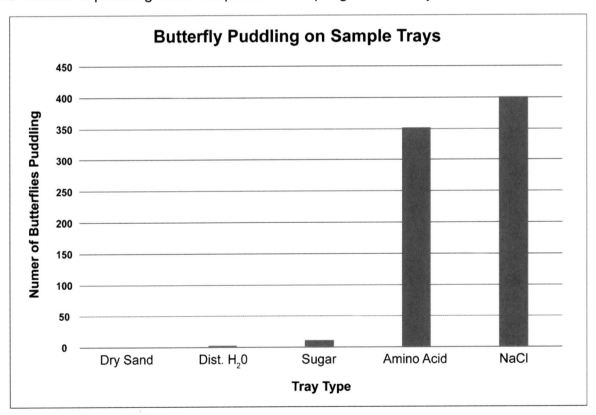

12-no

13-There were high numbers of puddling butterflies in the amino acid and sodium trays. The other three trays had little puddling.

14-This study did not determine the one reason why tiger swallowtail butterflies puddle.

15-The study did find that the butterflied do not puddle on dry sand, sand and water, or sand and sugar.

Study of Life

Characteristics of Life: Invertebrates

Life Functions	Hydra	Earthworm	Grasshopper
Environmental Response	Nerve Net; All or none response	Nervous System	Change color/form swarms (locusts); nervous system/senses
Growth	When bud gets big enough it falls off & lives independently	Can regenerate	Immature/molting stages
Reproduction	Budding-asexual/ sexual- hermaphroditic	Hermaphrodites	Hatch eggs
Evolve	Simpler 1 celled eukaryotes (sponges)	Simpler multi-celled eukaryotes with bilateral symmetry	Simpler multi-celled eukaryotes with bilateral symmetry
Nutrition	Opening ingests & egests food; tentacles bring food to mouth	Feeds on live & dead things	Omnivores/herbivores
Homeostasis	Diffusion across thin body wall & Nerve net	Closed circulation system & Coelom for gases, food, & waste	Heart pumps blood through body & regulated respiratory system & sheds exo-skeleton
Excretion	Diffusion of ammonia out of cells	Elimination of urea via nephridia "kidney"	Tubules remove wastes & form uric acid which is eliminated via digestive system
Regulation	Nerve net: all or none response	Nervous system	Nervous system
Transport	Gastroderm has a flagella	Coelom- fluid filled cavity closed circulatory system	Open circulatory system
Locomotion	Somersault; sessile	Muscles for movement	Jump- legs/wings

Demonstrating Diffusion and Osmosis/The Egg Lab

1-egg

2-cell

3-semi-/selectively permeable

4-diffusion

5-water

6-cytoplasm

7-Outer covering of animal cell; movement of molecules from an area of high concentration to low concentration using no energy; movement of water molecules from an area of high concentration to low concentration using no energy

8-white, oval, cold/smooth/hard

9-Answers vary.

10-Answers vary.

11-It should be less.

12-yellow/clear; larger/oval; soft/bouncy

13-It got larger.

14-in

15-less liquid in the jar; egg is bigger

16-it dissolved

17-acetic acid

18-Answers vary.

19-Answers vary.

20-more

21-yellow/clear; mushed oval; like a "bean bag"

22-smaller

23-out

24-more liquid in the jar; the egg is smaller

25-Answers vary.

26-Answerv vary.

27-less

28-yellow/white/clear; oval; bouncy

29-Much bigger

30-in

31-less liquid in the jar; the egg is bigger

32-water

33-Water does not have any other substances in it, it is "pure" (100%) water.

34-There is more water in a cell than in syrup.

35-Water diffuses into the fruit/vegetable cells through the process of osmosis.

36-It dehydrates the plant cells.

37-The water leave the cells because the water concentration is higher inside the cells than outside.

38-The water concentration is higher in the pot the fruit/beans are cooking in. Therefore, the water will move into the fruit/beans through the process of osmosis.

Examining Plant and Animal Cells

1-2 onion cells traced in red on 10x

2-bigger

3-less

4-2 onion cells traced on 40x

5-Nuclei may or may not be labeled

6-3 areas of cytoplasm labeled

7-2 onion cell walls traced in red under 40x after stained with iodine

8-2 onion cell membranes traced in blue under 40x after stained with iodine

9-cytoplasm labeled in two cells

10-nuclei labeled

11-to better see cell parts/organelles

12-kills living tissue

13-Elodea cells under 10x traced in red

14-bigger

15-less

16-two elodea cells under 40x traced in red

17-nuclei labeled

18-cytoplasm labeled in two cells

19-three chloroplasts labeled

20-Two animal cells under 10x traced in red

21-bigger

22-Two animal cells under 40x traced in red

23-nuclei labeled

24-cytoplasm labeled in two cells

25-Animal cells are more circular; onion plant cells are blocky/rectangular

26-Two animal cells stained with methylene blue under 40x are traced in blue

27-cytoplasm labeled

28-nuclei labeled

29-to see organelles

30-kills living cells

31-plant cells – squarish, cell wall, chloroplast, big vacuoles, no centrioles, no lysosomes; animal cells- circular, no cell wall, no chloroplasts, vesicles, centrioles, have lysosomes

32-bigger

33-fewer

34-to make cell parts more visible

35-adjust the amount of light

36-chloroplasts

37-centrioles

38-wall

39-vacuoles

40-vesicles

Understanding Microscopes and Microscopic Measurement

Introduction

1-10x

2-40x

3-100x

4-400x

5-Magnification Chart

Low Power: 10x, 10x, 100x

High Power: 10x, 40x, 400x

6-bigger, upside down, backwards

7-An upside down, magnified, backwards "e" should be drawn in the field of view.

8-moves towards me

9-moves away from me

10-moves to the left

11-moves to the right

12-The enlarged crossbar of the "e" should be drawn in the field of view.

13-There is a smaller field of view.

14-Lines from metric ruler should be sketched in the field of view; typically, there should be one center line and two partial lines on each side of the field

15-1

16-2 mm

17-1000 µm

18-2000 µm

19-100x

20-400x

21-2000 µm

22-Math work calculating diameter of how-power field of view should be shown.

23-2000 µm, 500 µm

24-1000 µm

25-400 µm

26-A "-" should be drawn enlarged in the field of view.

27-400 µm

28- 250 µm

29- 100 µm

Bibliography

Observing Photosynthesis: https://www.ducksters.com/science/photosynthesis.php

Classifying Animals: http://www.biology4kids.com/files/studies_taxonomy.html

Animal Phyla Cards:

https://commons.wikimedia.org/wiki/File:Acropora_muricata_Macro_Maldives.jpg#filelinks

https://commons.wikimedia.org/wiki/File:Actinopyga_echinites_R%C3%A9union.jpg

http://www.aphotofauna.com/worm_flatworm_australoplana_sanguinea.html

https://commons.wikimedia.org/wiki/File:Cardinalis_cardinalis_-Columbus,_Ohio,_USA-male-8_(1).jpg

https://www.poppe-images.com/?t=17&photoid=932707

https://commons.wikimedia.org/wiki/File:Compsobuthus_acutecarinatus_(1).JPG

https://en.wikipedia.org/wiki/Euglandina_rosea#/media/File:Euglandina_rosea.jpg

https://commons.wikimedia.org/wiki/File:Eunice_pennata.jpg

https://commons.wikimedia.org/wiki/File:Fromia_monilis_(Sea_star).jpg

https://en.wikipedia.org/wiki/File:Common_brimstone_butterfly_(Gonepteryx_rhamni)_male.jpg

https://commons.wikimedia.org/wiki/File:Gorgonia_ventalina.jpg

http://www.animalspot.net/blue-ringed-octopus.html

https://www.biolib.cz/en/image/id292151/

https://commons.wikimedia.org/wiki/File:Litoria_tyleri.jpg

http://www.nhptv.org/natureworks/stripedskunk.htm

https://commons.wikimedia.org/wiki/File:Mesostoma_ehrenbergii.jpg

https://commons.wikimedia.org/wiki/File:Obama_anthropophila_1.JPG

https://commons.wikimedia.org/wiki/File:Tonicella-lineata.jpg

https://commons.wikimedia.org/wiki/File:Tripneustes_ventricosus_(West_Indian_Sea_Egg)_edit.jpg

https://commons.wikimedia.org/wiki/File:Varroa_Mite.jpg

Dichotomous Keys:

https://www.isd2135.k12.mn.us/cms/lib/MN01001544/Centricity/Domain/54/Shark%20Dichotomous%20Key%20Lab.pdf

Understanding Taxonomy: https://animaldiversity.org/

Adapted for Survival? Bird Adaptations to Habitat:
https://www.coastal.ca.gov/publiced/waves/waves_7.pdf

Antibiotic Resistance:
http://static.nsta.org/connections/middleschool/201312WelbornWorksheetAnswers.pdf

Describing Elements of Evolution: https://ncse.com/files/pub/evolution/Evolution--Futuyma--chap11.pdf

Where do Pandas Fit in the Tree of Life?:
https://teach.genetics.utah.edu/content/evolution/ancestry/pdfs/panda-case-study.pdf

Animal Body Plans: Homeobox Genes: https://learn.genetics.utah.edu/content/basics/hoxgenes/

Digestive System: https://kidshealth.org/en/teens/digestive-system.html

Understanding Viruses: http://www.humanillnesses.com/original/U-Z/Viral-Infections.html

Observing the Cell Cycle in Onion Root Tips: https://www.thoughtco.com/understanding-the-cell-cycle-373391

Diagramming Embryological Development: http://www.newworldencyclopedia.org/entry/Germ_layer

Scientific Design—Ethics & Experimenter Bias: https://www.visionlearning.com/en/library/Process-of-Science/49/Scientific-Ethics/161

Characteristics of Life: Invertebrates: https://www.ducksters.com/animals/grasshopper.php

Request for Reviews

I sincerely hope you enjoyed using this educational tool as much as I enjoyed writing it. If you did, I would greatly appreciate a short review on Amazon or your favorite book or instructional materials website. Reviews are crucial for letting others know of the value of any instructional resource, and even just a line or two can make a huge difference.

Connect with The Author

G. Katz Chronicle has over three decades of teaching experience in primary, secondary, and higher education. Having taught all major content areas in primary and middle school, as well as education theory and biology at the secondary and college level, she most enjoys teaching the Life Sciences.

With a PhD in Curriculum and Instruction, she, too, is a perpetual student of traditional education and all areas of self-improvement.

G. Katz is an abbreviated form of Gertrude Katz. Gertrude maintains a Biology Teaching Blog where she provides her general instructional plans, reasoning, and thoughts for the NY State Living Environment Course. The blog consists of ten posts, which correspond to ten instructional units, and include unit presentations and videos. Gertrude invites you to check it out at: GertrudeKatzChronicle.com. Connect with her on other social media, as well!

Made in the USA
Las Vegas, NV
06 March 2024

86764251R00159